# Fundamental Aspects of Finding and Using Information

**Note**

Health care practice and knowledge are constantly changing and developing as new research and treatments, changes in procedures, drugs and equipment become available.

The author and publishers have, as far as is possible, taken care to confirm that the information complies with the latest standards of practice and legislation.

# Fundamental Aspects of Finding and Using Information

A Guide for Students of Nursing and Health

*Barbara Freeman and David Thompson*

QUAY
BOOKS

A division of MA Healthcare Ltd

Quay Books Division, MA Healthcare Ltd, St Jude's Church, Dulwich Road, London
SE24 0PB

British Library Cataloguing-in-Publication Data
A catalogue record is available for this book

© MA Healthcare Limited 2009

ISBN-10: 1 85642 369 7
ISBN-13: 978 1 85642 369 4

Printed by CLE, St Ives, Cambridgeshire

# Foreword

There is a vast amount of information in books, journals and (not least) electronic format on the internet. A simple Google search with the word 'nursing' has just given me 130,000,000 'hits' – which if my reading of zeros is correct, is one hundred and thirty million references. I've just worked out that if I spent two minutes looking at each reference, I would be spending the next 49 years of my life in continuous reading, with no time for sleep, food, or visits to the loo!

So how do we manage the vast amount of information at our fingertips? How can we find out which of those 130 million hits are relevant, valid and reliable?

The problem we have as health care workers is not the lack of information on which to inform our practice, but the fact that there is so much information from so many different sources.

A significant part of all health care professionals' training is now built around how to find information, evaluate the vast variety of data bases, access on line journals and generally handle the 130 million hits that we often get when looking for information.

This excellent short book is written by two experts in the field of health care information organisation. Barbara Freeman and David Thompson are both librarians who have worked for many years in a university library specialising in health care information. They have been key players in the introduction of the huge electronic systems that now form such an important part of data access within our library systems. Much of their working lives has been spent teaching students how to access and use information, while also providing additional one-to-one support for individual students in the library setting. This book is the fruit of that expert knowledge and practical applications.

Never before has one book on this topic been such a single core resource for health care students.

John Fowler
*Phd MA BA DipN Cert.Ed. RGN RMN RCNT RNT*
*Principal Lecturer in Nursing*
*De Montfort University*
*Series Editor*
*Fundamental Aspects of Nursing*

# Contents

# Introduction

In this book we aim to show that finding and using good quality information is a lot less difficult than you might think. Knowing how to use the resources available to you via libraries and the Internet efficiently brings much quicker, and better, results than trying to find information in a hit and miss kind of way, and doesn't require advanced IT skills. Just follow the simple strategies outlined in this volume and you will gain the basic information-seeking skills that are all you need to get started.

As you become more confident, your ability to evaluate sources will develop too. You will surprise yourself – not just by finding information, but by starting to ask yourself just how good that information is.

## How nurses use information

In January 2008 the *Nursing Standard* published an article by Rosalind Bertulis, of the Royal College of Nursing, based on a literature review of nurses' use of information for evidence-based practice (Bertulis 2008). She found that 'perceived lack of time' and lack of information technology skills are the main barriers preventing nurses from accessing information . She also found that nurses 'tend to base the selection of information sources on convenience and accessibility rather than quality'.

Clearly, accurate information and knowledge are vital, and a successful practitioner in the 21st century needs to be able to continue to acquire and effectively manage up-to-date, quality information. He or she needs to have effective 'information skills'.

## What are 'information skills'?

The three key information skills that we shall cover in this book are:

- **Finding** – knowing when, where and how to search for appropriate information
- **Evaluating** – judging the quality of the information you have found
- **Using** – referencing comprehensively and accurately to ensure that the work of others is acknowledged.

## How this book is organised

The contents of this volume fall into four key areas:

- **Getting started** – some things you need to think about before you launch into your quest for information; what help is at hand from libraries and electronic sources; and advice on what you can, can't and should do.
- **Books** – finding and using information from that most traditional of sources, books, and related media such as e-books and recordings.
- **Journal articles** – understanding the tools that are available to you to find references and access journal articles – possibly the area that many students struggle with most.
- **Internet resources** – using the Internet efficiently and critically to find good quality websites with a wealth of information including statistics, images, patient information and the evidence base for health care.

Our concluding chapter suggests ways in which you might want to follow up the research you have, hopefully, initiated after reading this volume. Whether you now want to move on to actually writing your assignment, or simply want to keep in touch with new developments in your chosen area, we provide useful hints and recommend some helpful additional reading.

## How to use this book

It really is up to you. We all learn in different ways, and it would be presumptuous of the authors to suggest that one way of using the book is better than any other. However, our aim from the start has been to make a book that can be dipped into – with cross-references and a reliable index enabling students to focus on what is important for them. At the same time we have set out to create a narrative which develops logically, and stands being read from cover to cover.

# Our background

This book is based on our experience of working directly with nursing and midwifery students in a specialist health library at De Montfort University, a leading centre of nursing and midwifery education. We are well aware of the difficulties and anxieties many students experience in trying to find the right information for academic assignments and hope in this book to give you more confidence in approaching your information searching.

Some of our examples are based on our own library, and we are aware that libraries of other libraries may differ in some details – but the essentials remain the same. Check out your library and the services available to you, and if in doubt about anything, ask library staff.

# Target audience

This book is intended for nursing, midwifery and health care students at under-graduate level. This includes everyone from first year pre-registration students through to practitioners studying for further specialist qualifications.

We hope you find the contents useful, and enjoy the experience of discovering more about information skills relating to your chosen profession.

# Reference

Bertulis, R. (2008) Barriers to accessing evidence-based information. *Nursing Standard*, 14 May, **22**(36), pp. 35–39.

# PART I

# **Getting started**

# CHAPTER I

# Know your library

## In this chapter

- Which libraries can you use?
- How libraries are organised
- Where can you get help?
- SCONUL Access

A better title for this chapter might have been 'Know your libraries', because whether student or employee, or indeed both, you have access to a wide range of libraries – not just the one where you work or study. Take a few moments to think about what resources are available to you, and the number may surprise you. Typically a student will have access to most or all of the following:

- Specialist health/nursing library
- Large multi-subject university library
- Workplace library
- Other university libraries
- National Library for Health
- RCN library (and libraries of other professional bodies)
- Public libraries

Almost without exception these libraries will have websites where you can discover a great deal about the services and resources offered, and their availability. Most will offer extensive 'virtual' facilities, so distance is no longer the often insurmountable barrier it once was.

Online catalogues are the norm nowadays, and access to full text journals grows more important by the day. E-books are predicted to be the next big growth area. In general, the library catalogue is likely to be accessible to any web user, but e-journals and e-books will be password controlled to permit access only to their registered students.

This chapter looks at the range of libraries available to you, how they are organised, and how to make the best use of them.

# 1.1 Which libraries can you use?

### Specialist health/nursing library

Nursing, midwifery and other health professions came into higher education only recently, and because of this there is a great variety in the kinds of library provision for these subject areas.

Many students and workers will find their 'home' library is a small specialist unit. Specialist libraries offer many benefits, but there can also be downsides. Among the benefits are the fact that all the resources will be relevant and in one place. In a multi-subject library, on the other hand, you may have to hunt around several floors to find all the material relevant to your work. Staff at a specialist library will also be highly focused and knowledgeable about your area of study.

Among the disadvantages may be restricted opening hours – perhaps not open at weekends or during the evenings – and less sophisticated IT facilities.

Many specialist libraries, however, will be part of a bigger library network. This bigger network will give you access to a wider range of resources and there may be more than one library that you can use. It may also offer weekend opening and (increasingly frequently nowadays) 24/7 opening at peak periods.

### Large multi-subject university library

Most students are likely to have access to such a facility. Even if your course is based on a small campus with its own specialist library, it is usually the case that you are part of a bigger network.

As just discussed, access to such a facility can bring many benefits in terms of study facilities, access to resources and opening hours. Just because your course is based on a small campus, do not assume there is nothing relevant to you at the 'main site'. There may well be courses available on related areas such as social care and health policy whose resources you can take advantage of.

### Workplace library

All hospitals and many health care facilities will have their own library facilities. These will also be available to students on placement at those sites – usually through the 'SCONUL Access' scheme which is outlined later in this chapter.

### Other university libraries

Students may find it more convenient to use a university library other than the one where they are studying – especially if they live some distance from their place of study. If you are a full time student the SCONUL Access scheme will allow you access for reference purposes. If you are a part-time student, or on placement, then you will be allowed to borrow a limited number of books. More details of the scheme are provided later in this chapter.

### National Library for Health

The National Library for Health (NLH) is a very important library which exists only as an online resource. Set up by the NHS to be the definitive knowledge base for staff and patients, it can be accessed at http://www.nlh.nhs.uk/. See Chapter 17 for more on the NLH.

### Libraries of professional bodies

Many professional bodies have their own libraries which are available to their members. Examples include:

- Royal College of Nursing
  Libraries in London, Edinburgh, Cardiff and Belfast, as well as smaller Resource Centres around the country. Details can be found at:

  http://www.rcn.org.uk/library/

- Royal College of Midwives
  Library in London. More details are at:

  http://www.rcm.org.uk/info/pages/library/

However, you may find that some of the services offered, such as supplying photocopies of journal articles, work out considerably more expensive than the same service from your own library. Some libraries will offer to search for information for you, at a cost, which is very tempting to a student hard-pressed for time. On balance, however, it's probably better that you learn to do things for yourself: it will make you independent, and save you money too.

### Public libraries

Last, but not least – don't forget public libraries. They offer more than cheap fiction and dusty archives. That book that's never on the shelves at the university may well be ready and waiting just round the corner at the public library. As is now common for all libraries, you will be able to check out a great deal on their websites. But once again – be careful about making reservations and making photocopies. Charges will almost always be in excess of what you might expect to pay at your place of study.

## 1.2 How libraries are organised

Whole books are written about how libraries are organised. That is not the aim of this book, which sets out to provide a user-friendly introduction to information skills. However, a small amount of knowledge will help students gain confidence in using libraries, saving time and effort later on.

There are six key areas where students should aim to be up to speed. Crack these and everything else should fall into place. To be an ace library user, you should know:

- How to use and understand the library catalogue
- What collections (books, journals, theses etc.) are available and how to access them
- Which material can be borrowed, and for how long? When is the library open?
- What IT equipment is available; how do you access it?
- How much can be accessed online from home or work?
- What help is available

The Appendix at the back of this book shows you the two schemes for arranging libraries that you are most likely to encounter.

**How to use and understand the library catalogue**

The library catalogue, which is almost certainly available online, is absolutely fundamental to tracking down library resources. You will find much, much more about the catalogue in a number of subsequent chapters – particularly, as you might expect, those chapters looking at finding books and journals.

Here is not the place to repeat what is said in those chapters, but in summary we would say:

- Be aware of the searching hints given in those chapters, especially the need to be accurate, and to keep things simple.
- Know how to interpret the information the catalogue gives you in terms of how many copies should be on the shelf, which collection they are in, which copies are on loan, when they are due back etc.
- Make sure you know how to reserve books.

**How many different collections are available?**

Even quickly skimming this book should leave you with the impression that books and journals are without doubt the two key resources provided by academic libraries. But most libraries will have a number of other collections, which you need to understand if you are going to (a) find them, and (b) make best use of them.

The exact range will vary from library to library. Apart from books and journals, typically you can expect to find:

- **Reference books**: dictionaries, directories, atlases etc.
- **Short loan books**: collections of books heavily in demand. These copies will be available just for a short period, such as overnight so that everyone has a chance to read the relevant material. The collection may be called something different, such as Overnight Loan, Course Texts etc.
- **Audio-visual material**: DVDs, slides, models etc.
- **Oversize/pamphlets**: items whose size or format means they have to be stored separately.
- **Stack/store**: rarely used items may be stored in a basement, or at a remote location. You may need to give 24 hours' notice that you wish to see these items.
- **Dissertations**: usually held separately in a secure area. You will need to ask a librarian to obtain these for you.
- **Photocopies**: some key texts or articles may only be available as photocopies. Access may be via a librarian. These collections come under a variety of names: 'missing pages' and 'off-prints' are just two that we have come across.

As well as knowing where to find these materials, you also need to be aware that borrowing rules are also likely to vary. Some different types of audio-visual material may only be loanable for 24 hours or 7 days, for instance. Other material, such as theses, may be reference only.

### What, when, how?

To ensure a smooth and successful library experience you'll fare better if you are familiar with basic 'rules and regs'. It will help greatly if you know:

- How many books you can borrow
- What other materials can be borrowed
- How long items can be kept
- Whether items can be renewed
- What the charges are for late return of books
- When the library is open. Is it the same during vacations?

All this information will almost certainly be available from the library's website. And there will be other rules about quiet working areas, group working areas, food and drink, use of mobile phones etc. All aim to provide a good study environment for those who wish to use it.

### What IT equipment is available?

Besides computers and photocopiers a wide range of other IT equipment may be available for you to use:

- Colour printers
- Scanners
- Laptop computers for loan within the library
- Data projectors and screens, for preparing and practising presentations

We talk more about IT in the next chapter.

### How much can I do from home?

The rise of online learning means that much of your information seeking and learning can now be done at home, without stepping foot anywhere near the library. What is available, and how you can achieve this, will vary from institution to institution.

As a minimum requirement you will need to understand how to login to the various services. Beyond this, much that you need to know will be published on the library website, with library staff available for further help as required.

All these issues are looked at in more detail in the next chapter.

## 1.3 Where can you get help?

Library staff, just like health workers, love to be able to help – it's why most of us came into this profession. So don't be afraid to ask for help – and no, your question is not a silly one, we will probably have heard it before! But remember, the person who is the most accessible to you in the library may not necessarily be the person who is best placed to help you with your query. Look for a designated Enquiry or Information point, which will be staffed by a person who will either know the answer to your query or know someone who does. You can also normally either phone or email a query – look for details on leaflets or library guides.

### Extra help needed

Librarians are very well aware that some students will need extra help because of a disability. This might be a physical disability which could make getting around the library difficult, a sensory one such as a visual or hearing problem, or, very commonly, dyslexia. Some students may have more than one disability.

Libraries usually have very good provision for supporting students with disabilities, both because the law insists on it and because we want our students to have the best possible experience. Some provision will be apparent, such as ramps, lifts or hearing loops. Other services won't be, such as extended loans periods for students with dyslexia, or special software that can help with either dyslexia or visual difficulties. You may need to ask what help is available. Most university libraries with have a designated librarian with whom you can discuss your needs in total confidence and who will be able to tell you what help is available.

## 1.4 SCONUL Access

SCONUL Access is a cooperative arrangement between most higher education libraries in the UK and Ireland. Run by SCONUL (the Society of College, National and University Libraries), this enables staff, research students, full-time postgraduates, and part-time, distance learning and placement students to borrow material from other libraries.

The scheme does not permit borrowing by full-time students, but it does allow them reference use of other libraries.

To take advantage of the scheme, first visit your home university library to register for SCONUL Access. Provided you are in 'good standing' (no major fines or long overdue books) you will be issued with a SCONUL Access card which you then need to take (with your home library card) to the library you wish to use.

To find out more about the scheme and whether your home library is a member, check the SCONUL Access website at: http://www.access.sconul. ac.uk/.

# CHAPTER 2

# Know your IT

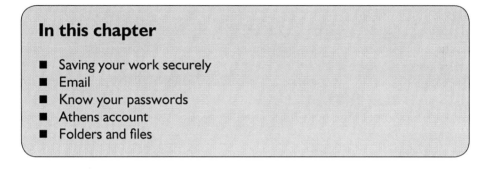

**In this chapter**

- Saving your work securely
- Email
- Know your passwords
- Athens account
- Folders and files

Like it or loathe it, studying today cannot be divorced from IT, and it will help immensely if you can develop some basic IT proficiencies. Recent IT developments have revolutionised much of the learning process, bringing powerful searches for information to your fingertips. In just five minutes at home it is now possible to do things which previous generations would have taken many days and countless trips to a host of locations to achieve.

It is now so effective that some traditional sources of information are no longer available in printed format. In the future this trend seems set to continue, and indeed accelerate.

Strategically the NHS has recognised the importance of IT in the nursing profession, but the reality of everyday life for nurses is that access to computers is simply not on offer. And with many nurses now taking up post-registration training, the learning curve in adapting to an IT environment that was simply non-existent during the years of their own formal education can be steep.

This section offers some key IT tips for students starting a new course of study.

## 2.1 Save often and save securely

The importance of ensuring that you always have a saved version of your work, along with a backup, is probably the single most important lesson you can learn from this chapter. Always make sure that you have a second copy of your file – and that both files are somewhere accessible. And don't forget to save the words you wrote just a few minutes ago – don't wait a couple of hours until you are tired and hungry before you save: hunger or fatigue might cause you to forget, or simply press the keys in the wrong order.

Until recently floppy disks have been a favourite means of saving work. This is fine until the floppy disk becomes corrupt for whatever reason. If all your work is saved in just one place, and you can then no longer access it, you might understandably become very upset. The secret is to plan ahead, use reliable devices, and above all ensure you have backed your work up.

Many academic institutions offer services such as 'NetStorage' which allow students to store work on a central server (computer) which they can access from home, from college, or from work. Each student will be allocated a generous amount of space for their work. Other students will not be able to see your work, and you won't be able to see theirs. This is an excellent way of backing up your work, and you would be strongly advised to use it.

Memory sticks (USBs) are rapidly becoming the preferred means of saving files in a portable format. These are far more reliable than floppy disks and can carry huge amounts of information. Prices were fairly prohibitive until recently, but are coming down fast. This is all well and good, but do not let yourself be lulled into a false sense of security! Being small and portable brings disadvantages as well as benefits – memory sticks are easily lost, and the need for back up remains. You might want to add a file to the memory stick indicating your contact details, just in case someone finds it and tries to return it to you.

And of course, whatever your preferred format, you will lose your work by simply forgetting to save the latest changes you have made. So do get into the habit of always saving your work regularly, both to the computer and to your backup device. Best practice is to keep *saving as you work* – say every 20

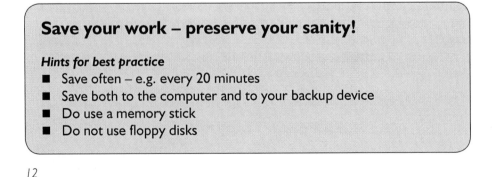

### Save your work – preserve your sanity!

*Hints for best practice*
- Save often – e.g. every 20 minutes
- Save both to the computer and to your backup device
- Do use a memory stick
- Do not use floppy disks

minutes or so. You are then covered for completely unforeseen situations such as computer failure or power cuts.

## 2.2 Email

Students starting new courses can expect to be given an academic email account. If you already have email at both home and work, you may well feel that a third email account is something of an imposition.

However, the new student email address will be the main, and often the only, means of communication between the institution and yourself, and it is important that you get in to the habit of checking it regularly. Key password and PIN information are more than likely going to be sent to the academic email address.

Information about library reservations, recalls and overdues, as well as other news such as temporary and unforeseen changes and closures are also likely to be sent to your student email address. The same will be true for communications from your tutors and fellow students. Some institutions will use email to advise you of found property – such as that memory stick containing all your assignment work which you left in a library PC!

## 2.3 Passwords, passwords, passwords

Information, like money, is power. You do not want just anyone dipping in to your bank account. Likewise you do not want just any student stealing your ideas, or using money from your virtual print balance to pay for their own printing.

To ensure you work in a safe environment your university will provide various user names and passwords. There are moves to simplify password systems in the future, and if you are lucky the 'Shibboleth' system may be in force already where you study. However, for many students, the sad fact is there will be at least three separate password or PIN systems covering different aspects of your studies.

You are likely to need passwords for some or all of the following:

- Accessing computers
- Printing and photocopying
- Requesting and renewing books using automated systems
- Accessing your student email
- Accessing databases

- Accessing the virtual learning environment (sometimes known as VLE or blackboard)
- Accessing the managed learning environment (MLE)
- Making e-payments

Some of these applications will share passwords, but there is no arguing about the fact that this is complicated – especially for new students who may have little previous experience of using IT in a learning environment. The best advice can only be – make a clear and accessible record of each (including what it is for); and, just like a banking PIN, do not share you details with colleagues. It is also a good idea not to delete any emails which have been sent to you containing your password details.

### What if I forget my password?

If you don't know your password, have forgotten it or can't use it for any other reason, library staff will help you. They may well be able to provide a new password; if not, they will know how to go about arranging one for you.

Sometimes you may be able to sort this out yourself. For instance, the Athens system described below allows you to set up a new password by email.

## 2.4 Athens accounts

In the information world Athens isn't nearly as exciting as it sounds, but it is your password to a whole world of essential information!

Almost all the key databases and e-journals that you want to access are password-protected, and nearly all of these use the same password – the Athens password. Databases are expensive items and your institution will only want those students who are entitled to use them to have access.

The Athens account is a national scheme set up to verify that database users belong to institutions that have subscribed. If you are a university student you should find that your Athens account has been created for you already and details will probably be emailed to you. The account will consist of a username which will include something to identify the institution you belong to, and a password unique to you. The password will be a random selection of letters and numbers which may not be the easiest to remember.

| **My user names and passwords** |
|---|

| **Computers** | |
|---|---|
| Username | |
| Password | |

| **Athens** | |
|---|---|
| Required to access BNI (British Nursing Index) and many other databases | |
| Username | |
| Password | |

| **Email** | |
|---|---|
| Username | |
| Password | |

| **VLE (Virtual Learning Environment)** | |
|---|---|
| Username | |
| Password | |

| **Photocopying** | |
|---|---|
| Username | |
| Password | |

| **PIN** | |
|---|---|
| Make a note of applications when you need to use your PIN | |

Noting your passwords in a grid like this will help bring peace of mind. Add comments where necessary, and remember that the exact range of passwords required will vary from university to university.

**Figure 2.1** Keeping track of your passwords.

### *My Athens password is difficult to remember – can I change it?*

If you decide to change your password to something more memorable, you can do that by going to MyAthens: http://ap3.auth.athensams.net/my/ and clicking on the 'MyAccount' tab. You will then see an option for changing your password.

**What about the NHS Athens account?**

The NHS also uses Athens accounts to allow its staff to access databases etc. If you are an NHS staff member you are entitled to an NHS Athens account which you can create yourself. It's best to do this from a computer which is on the NHS network because then you are easily recognised as NHS staff and the process is quicker. Information about NHS Athens passwords and how to set one up is available at http://www.library.nhs.uk/athens/.

**Do I need both?**

Probably yes, as each gives access to a slightly different range of databases, and it's worth having both to give you the widest range of available resources. You may also find that when you log on to a database in your University library your NHS Athens account isn't accepted; in an NHS library a University account may not be.

**Not all databases use Athens**

Unfortunately, some databases and e-journals do not use Athens to verify users but have their own usernames and passwords. The full archives of *Nursing Standard* or *Nursing Times*, for example, require a different sort of password. Individual NHS staff are able to log on at no charge to *Nursing Times*, but you will have to register and use an assigned user name and password.

More typical is *Nursing Standard*, to which your institution probably subscribes, but you will need to know the institution's user name and password. You will normally be able to find these on your library's website, but if not – ask a librarian.

**Athens is changing...**

Moves towards simplifying student access to computers and databases by developing a 'single sign on' for all services are gathering pace. Unfortunately, this leaves some institutions in something of a halfway house at present and things may appear even more complicated.

You may well see something like 'Log in via UK Federation' and then have to select your university from a list, before entering an appropriate password, which may be Athens or it may be one called 'Shibboleth'.

If you are in any doubt about logins, our best advice is – as ever – ask your librarian.

## 2.5 Folders, files and other IT features

After email, word processing is probably the IT feature most heavily used by most students. And once you get started, the files will mount up, possibly to the extent that you have trouble finding the work you did just a couple of days ago.

At this point one of the benefits of using computers – the easy retrieval of information – is in danger of being lost. However, your computer can organise this for you as well, provided you get to grips with setting up folders for your files. This is something you can learn in seconds, and you will rapidly reap the rewards.

There are many other hints and tips for making best use of the computer to help you learn and write – from using tables and graphics to management of footnotes. It is not the intention of this book to provide in-depth coverage of all these possible IT skills – excellent introductions to this area are provided by a number of books which are readily available. A good example is Chapter 3, 'Using a computer to study', in Northedge (2005).

## Reference

Northedge, A. (2005). *The good study guide*. Milton Keynes: Open University Press.

# Keeping records

This is a very short chapter, but the topic it covers is a very important one. We will return to this issue later in the book, but as our readers will be enthusiastic students raring to get started, we make no apology for raising this issue at an early stage.

## 3.1 Why keep records?

As you carry out your studies you will undoubtedly find many useful books and articles, along with much which appears less helpful at first glance, but which you think you might just want to come back to later.

For purely practical purposes you might well decide to keep a note of everything you find that comes anywhere near useful. But there are more compelling reasons for wanting to do so.

Firstly, when you come to hand in your work, your tutors will expect you to have referred to published information, and to show this by making reference to those sources in your essay or dissertation.

It is much easier, and you are more likely to get a successful result, if you keep tabs on what your sources are *as you use them*. Sometimes students forget to do this, and try to chase up the details just when the deadline for handing in is just hours away.

Anyone who has tried to find again something they found so easily just a couple of days again will know how difficult this can be. It can take hours of searching, and sometimes you never do find it again.

A second important reason is to avoid any danger of plagiarism – i.e. appearing to pass off someone else's work as your own. Provided you keep records of what you have referred to, and make proper reference to it in your essays, then you will have nothing to worry about.

We talk about referencing and plagiarism in much more detail in Chapter 4.

## 3.2 How to keep records

Possibly the simplest option is to keep a word-processed file. By cutting and pasting, you will be able to maintain accurate details of the books you use.

Sometimes the catalogues and databases you use will provide additional options which allow easy saving of sources. Typically they will allow you to store relevant articles and titles in a folder, which you can then save to your computer or memory stick, or email to yourself (Figure 3.1). We will look at these possibilities in Chapters 6 and 12 when we look in detail at using catalogues and databases.

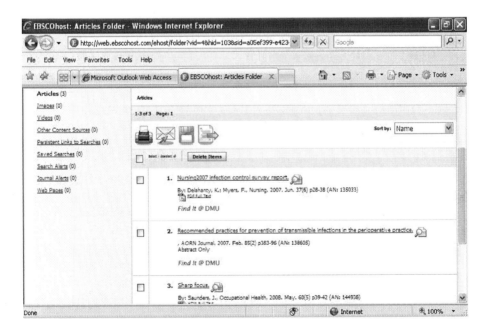

**Figure 3.1**

And finally, of course, you can keep handwritten notes. This is fine for those with perfect handwriting, and provided you copy all the details with absolute accuracy. It also helps if you have time to spare. If you cannot in all honesty tick each of those boxes, this is probably a method best consigned to history.

# CHAPTER 4

# 'Do's and 'don't's: some legal and academic considerations

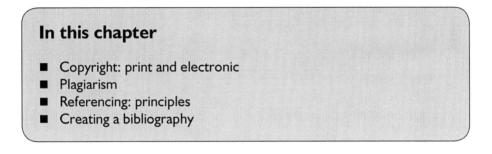

**In this chapter**

- Copyright: print and electronic
- Plagiarism
- Referencing: principles
- Creating a bibliography

## 4.1 Copyright

When you find useful information, perhaps in a book or a journal, you might feel that you want to take a copy of it so that you can be sure you have the information and can read it and make notes on it later when you have time. So you may be surprised to find that there are limits on what you can do, even though you are paying for your copying.

This is because UK law protects the rights of the creators of information by the Copyright, Designs and Patents Act 1988. The law is based on the concept of 'intellectual property' – if you have created information, then it belongs to you and you have rights over it that no one else does. In fact, it is not an idea, in itself, that is protected by copyright law – it is the expression of that idea in material form, such as a book, journal or recording.

This does not mean that you can't copy anything at all. In recognition of the needs of students and researchers, the concept of 'fair dealing' is applied. Fair dealing enables you to do a limited amount of copying for your own private study purposes. Just how much copying is permissible is not set out in the law, but is generally taken to be:

- Only one article from a single issue of a journal
- Only one chapter – not more than 5% – of a book

You should be making only one copy and should be able to say that, to the best of your knowledge, no other person with whom you are studying is copying the same material for the same purpose. So if you were working on a group project, not every member of the group could copy the same journal article.

**Figure 4.1** CILIP copyright advice. Poster reproduced by kind permission of CILIP.

Copying within the terms of fair dealing should not be too restrictive for you – it allows for most of what most students would wish to do.

You may find that your lecturers seem to be much more liberal in their photocopying. They may, for example, give every student in the class a copy of an important article. They are allowed to do this under the terms of a licence for Higher Education institutions. You may also find that what you are allowed to copy in your university library is different from what you are allowed in an NHS library. This is because different licensing arrangements are in place.

### Copying from electronic sources

The law relating to copying from printed materials has evolved over a long time, but so far there is no agreement as to what constitutes fair dealing in relation to electronically published information. People often feel that whatever is published on the Internet is 'up for grabs' and you can do whatever you want with it – but this is not so. The same principle applies: material published online is the intellectual property of its creator, whose rights are protected in law.

You can copy from an electronic source only single copies of limited amounts of material, which must be for private study. Just because it is easy to take copies of material found on the Internet doesn't make it legal. Check websites for any text relating to copyright, and if there is none, proceed with caution and bear in mind the principles of fair dealing.

In any breach of copyright law the responsibility lies with the individual making the copy, not with the providers of equipment such as library photocopiers or computers. Those signs by copiers telling you what you can and can't do are there to protect you!

You should:

- **Be aware** of legal restrictions on copying
- **Seek advice** from a librarian if in any doubt about copying

## 4.2 Plagiarism

Plagiarism means stealing the ideas or writings of others and passing them off as your own. It is regarded as the most serious of academic offences and a student found guilty of plagiarism could face a penalty ranging from an automatic fail for the assignment to being discontinued from the course. The Internet has made plagiarism easier and more tempting.

Some students feel that there is little likelihood of their being caught out in acts of plagiarism. But most universities now use specialist software such as 'Turnitin' which compares student work with published texts – and most lecturers are very astute at spotting work that just doesn't feel quite right!

Some acts of plagiarism are very blatant and quite easy to identify – if you copy an essay done by another student and simply put your name to it, that is clearly 'stealing the writings of others and passing them off as your own'. There are other lesser acts of 'ideas theft' that you may not think of as plagiarism – but they are.

According to the Open University, you are in danger of committing an offence by:

- Using a choice phrase or sentence that you have come across
- Copying directly from a text
- Paraphrasing the words from a text very closely
- Using text from the Internet
- Borrowing statistics or assembled facts from another person or source
- Copying or downloading figures, photographs, pictures or diagrams without acknowledging sources
- Copying from the notes or essays of a fellow student
- Copying from your own notes on a text, tutorial, video or lecture that contains direct quotes
- Collusion, or working with other students to produce a piece of work that was intended to be all your own work, is also regarded as a form of plagiarism.

Quite scary, isn't it?

Plagiarism is very easily avoided. You aren't expected to avoid using the work of others, only to acknowledge it appropriately. There are two rules:

- Know how to find information yourself; then you have no need to steal it from others
- Acknowledge the writer of every single idea, quotation, key phrase, statistic, or other piece of information that you use

In other words: reference, reference, reference.

If in doubt: reference.

If you have a juicy piece of information but can't trace where it came from – leave it out.

# 4.3 Referencing

These are the reasons why you must reference:

- To acknowledge the work of others and thus avoid any possibility of plagiarism
- To enable anyone reading your work to find and read the same sources of information that you have used
- To demonstrate that you understand and can follow the rules and conventions of academic writing

There are several different systems of referencing, which include Harvard, Vancouver and British Standard. In this book, the examples we shall give are of Harvard referencing, because it is the most widely used. As we look at each different kind of information we will give you a rough guide to referencing it, Harvard style, but you must follow the system required by your lecturers.

The basic principle of referencing is that when you refer to another person's work in your text, you mention it only briefly – name and date is usually enough – so that you don't interrupt the flow of your writing, and then give the full details at the end of the piece. Referencing systems differ mainly in the way the references are listed – either in alphabetical (Harvard) or numerical (Vancouver, British Standard) order, and in the exact order in which the information is recorded.

Whatever system you are using, your references must be:

- Correct
- Complete
- Consistent

We don't intend to go into great detail about referencing in this book, as there are already some excellent books and websites on the topic which we list at the end of this chapter. Your library may also have handouts or online information about the referencing system used in your institution.

There are various possible ways of introducing someone else's work in your text. Consider some of these:

- Brown and Blair (2008) believe that the increase in eating disorders...
- In their study of eating disorders among adolescent males Brown and Blair (2008) found that...
- One recent research study (Brown and Blair, 2008) showed that anorexia is more likely to be a problem...

- Brown and Blair (2008, p. 95) argued that 'whilst anorexia is regarded as a disorder affecting young women...'
- Brown and Blair (2008, p. 127) concluded that 'the number of boys and young men affected...'

If you are quoting a specific paragraph, you can give the number of the page it appears on. If you are summarising a general argument in a book or article, it won't be appropriate to quote specific page numbers.

Any of the above examples is correct – in each case you have an author and a date to correspond with the full details which will appear in your reference list. For the sake of the reader, try to use a variety of different methods to refer to information sources.

# 4.4 Create a bibliography

As well as your reference list you may also need to add a bibliography, which is a list of books and other materials that you have used to help you write your assignment, even though you have not referred directly to them in your final written piece. If you have read some general books or articles, looked at some relevant websites, or watched a DVD on the topic, then give yourself some credit for work done by listing them in a bibliography.

**Some useful guides to referencing**

*Books*

Neville, C. (2007) *The complete guide to referencing and avoiding plagiarism.* Maidenhead: Open University Press.
   *A very comprehensive guide to referencing covering different styles, with exercises and 'frequently asked questions'.*
Pears, R. and Shields, G. (2005) *Cite them right: the essential guide to referencing and plagiarism.* Newcastle upon Tyne: Pear Tree Books.
   *No-frills, easy to use guide to Harvard style.*

**Websites**

Bournemouth University (2008) *Citing references*. Available from: http://www.bourne-mouth.ac.uk/library/citing_references/.

*This is a comprehensive and easy to use guide. It includes a general guide to citation in the Harvard style and also a series of 'Quick guides to referencing' most materials.*

Your own university's website – most will have guides to the referencing system that students are required to follow.

# CHAPTER 5

# Literature search

## In this chapter

■ Defining and demystifying the literature search

We are now nearing the end of the 'Getting started' part of this book, and are about to move on to the nitty gritty of finding and using information. Before we start, however, it may be worth spending a few moments explaining what exactly is meant by a 'literature search'. It is a term you will come across in your studies and is very likely to be used by your tutors. Many students seem worried by the idea of a literature search but it is really a very simple concept.

In the context of information-finding for your studies, 'literature' means all the published information on your subject area – provided it is of a high enough academic standard. So we could be talking about books, reports, government publications, articles from academic journals, statistics – regardless of the physical form, paper or electronic, in which it exists.

A literature search, then, is the process of finding this suitable literature. The term 'search' implies an approach that is systematic and considered, rather than random or haphazard.

Sarah Gash (2000, p. 1) defines a literature search as 'a systematic and thorough search of all types of published literature in order to identify as many items as possible that are relevant to a particular topic.'

'Published' can mean published in any physical format – it includes books and journal articles, which may be printed or electronic; websites, even DVDs or television programmes.

The extent of the search that you will need to do is going to vary according to the nature of the assignment that you have been set. If you were a serious researcher, perhaps studying for a doctorate, you might well be expected to be aware of all the published (and even unpublished) literature on your chosen subject area. But happily for you, for most undergraduate assignments you would be looking for a much more modest amount of information. You may just be using a few journal articles to indicate that you have thought carefully and read around the subject you are writing about. You may want articles to illustrate different approaches to tackling the same problem, so that you can discuss them and show that you have considered these possibilities.

If you are writing an undergraduate dissertation in nursing or another health discipline, it may consist entirely of a review of the literature on your chosen topic, as ethical considerations prevent students from carrying out research with patients.

You should at least be able to answer these questions about your search:

- What sources have I used? (library catalogues, databases, search engines)
- What subject terms did I search for?
- What was the time span of my search?

Not every assignment is going to be in the form of an essay but every assignment will require some sort of literature searching. Any lecturer marking your work is going to be looking for some evidence of finding and using relevant information.

In the main sections of this book we shall look at the various component parts of a literature search, starting with books in the next chapter.

# Reference

Gash, S. (2000) *Effective literature searching for research*, 2nd ed. Aldershot: Gower.

# PART II

# Books

# CHAPTER 6

# Finding books

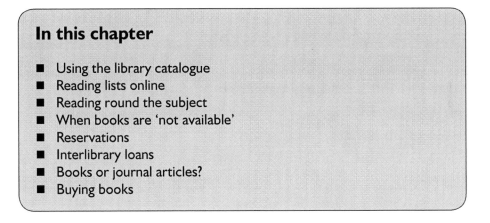

**In this chapter**

- Using the library catalogue
- Reading lists online
- Reading round the subject
- When books are 'not available'
- Reservations
- Interlibrary loans
- Books or journal articles?
- Buying books

For many years now, people have been predicting the end of the book. The Internet, they say, has taken over from the book as people's preferred method of finding information. Well, perhaps that time is coming, but in our library at least, it hasn't come yet! Students are still clamouring for books and the eternal complaint about their libraries is 'Not enough books!'.

Let's face it: there never will be enough books. If there are over 200 of you studying the same module, with the same assignment to do, and the same hand-in date for your work, then the library would need 200 copies of important books to meet everyone's needs. That just isn't going to happen – but what can happen is that you become a skilled library user and make sure you get the information you need.

## 6.1 Using the library catalogue

### Finding books on your reading list

Any academic module or course will have an accompanying reading list, which may include not just books, but a range of other formats including journal articles, recommended websites, and other materials which aren't really 'reading' at all – such as DVDs or CDs.

The first books that you are likely to want are the ones that are on your reading list for the assignment you are doing. To find out if the library has the book you need, you will need to use the library catalogue. This will be a computerised listing of the details of all the items in the library's stock, which you can search in many different ways. The library catalogue is sometimes called OPAC, which stands for Online Public Access Catalogue, or it may be called something like LibCat or WebCat.

The catalogue will almost certainly be available through the library website, enabling access from home and work. And it will tell you far more than whether the book is in stock – you will be able to see at a glance whether copies of the book are all on loan (and if so, you will usually be able to reserve the book), all within a couple of minutes while sat miles from your university library.

### Author and title searches

With your reading list in front of you, you will have the necessary details to search for a book – author, title, date of publication, edition, place of publication, publisher. The simplest form of search is by Author and Title. You will usually find that the principle of 'less is more' works here – in other words, the less information you put in, the more successful you are likely to be. In fact, in most cases you will need to input only two words maximum – one surname and the first word of the title (ignoring 'a' or 'the').

For example, imagine you were looking for a book that appeared on your reading list as:

Lillyman, S. and Ghaye, T. (2007) *Effective clinical supervision: the role of reflection*, 2nd ed. Chichester: Quay Books.

You now take the surname of the first author, and the first word of the title, and place them in the search box. Some catalogues require you to separate the author from the title. In these cases simply put one word in each, i.e.:

- you would put into the Author search box: Lillyman
- and into the Title search box: effective

This approach will almost certainly find what you are looking for. You would be shown details of all the editions the library holds, from which you would select the one you wanted.

If the author/title search suggested here should fail, try the same words, but this time put them both in the keyword field (or specify 'keyword' according to the catalogue format). This can be particularly useful where a new edition has a slightly different title, or has a new editor.

Search options for library catalogues vary greatly from institution to institution, and you may have to vary the details of how approach your search. But the overall guidance to 'keep it simple' and limit your terms to just two will invariably yield dividends.

### Books with no clear author

A book must have been written by someone, or a group of people, but sometimes it is almost impossible to find out just who. This is often the case with publications that come from government departments or other official bodies, where the book represents the outcome of the work of the whole department or organisation.

Sometimes it is not the lack of a name that is the problem, but the fact there are so many different organisations listed on the cover or title page. In these cases it can be very difficult to work out who is primarily responsible for the book.

In all these cases, where information is either lacking or totally confusing, don't worry about it: keep things simple. Just use a title search only (and as ever, keep it very short). You may have a few extra items to look through, but you have a far better chance of finding your book with no author than with the wrong one.

### Spelling, typing and other errors

Don't put too much faith in your reading list – your lecturer (or, indeed, the typist) is only human and mistakes do creep in! If you feel sure the book must be in the library, but you are having trouble finding it on the catalogue, at least consider the possibility that either the author or title may be misspelt on your list, and try other variations. Or, of course, you could have mistyped yourself – computer catalogues are quite unforgiving of spelling errors.

### Alternative spellings

By and large there is universal agreement over what is 'correct' spelling in English. But with new technology and ways of working, new concepts emerge, and it can be a few years before there is a generally agreed spelling.

Also, remember that much of the literature originates in, or is influenced by work in, the USA. Do keep in mind that accepted US spellings may differ from UK practice.

A selection of common alternatives is given in Table 6.1.

**Table 6.1** Alternative spellings.

| One word or two? |
| --- |
| Custom and practice are divided on whether some terms comprise one word or two, for example:<br><br>Health care or healthcare?<br><br>Hand washing or handwashing? |

| Hyphenated or not? |
| --- |
| Is it *evidence based* or *evidence-based*?<br><br>Could it be *health-care* and not *health care*? (See Figure 6.1) |

| American spelling? |
| --- |
| The catalogue may be sophisticated, but not clever enough to realise that *aging* is the same as *ageing*, or that *tumor* is the same as *tumour*. Likewise it may think *catheterisation* is a different word from *catheterization*. This is a particular issue with medical and nursing texts, where American publishing forms a significant element, and sometimes the only source, of available material. |

| UK spelling | US spelling |
| --- | --- |
| ageing | aging |
| anaemia | anemia |
| anaesthesia | anesthesia |
| behaviour | behavior |
| catheterisation | catheterization |
| foetus | fetus |
| gynaecology | gynecology |
| hospitalisation | hospitalization |
| organisation | organization |
| paediatric | pediatric |
| tumour | tumor |

**Figure 6.1** One word or two? Health care, health-care or healthcare?

### *The catalogue record*

When you search the catalogue, you may first of all see a list of books that doesn't look very helpful. It seems to suggest that the book is in the library, but doesn't tell you where it is. You may need to click once more – perhaps on something called 'Show copies' or 'Library holdings' to see the full details.

From this information you can confirm that you have the book you're looking for. You can also see:

- Which libraries have copies (if your institution has several sites with separate libraries)
- How many copies are in stock
- How many copies are on loan – and how many available to borrow
- Whether the book is kept in any special collection (e.g. short loan or reference)
- The shelf-mark or class-mark of this particular book

Notice at this stage whether the book should be on the shelves or not – a lot of time is wasted in searching the shelves for books that are already on loan. Make a note of the class-mark or shelf-mark – this is what you will need to find the book on the shelves.

## 6.2 Reading lists online

You may well find that librarians have put your module reading list online and linked it to various resources. In the best examples this facility takes away all the hard work – all the student has to do is click on the list, and the full recommended text appears – almost by magic – on the screen before you.

Sadly, the number of such 'full text' links is likely to be relatively small. Nevertheless, the existence of an online reading list can still take a lot of the drudgery out of checking your reading list.

At first glance the online list seems to offer little more than the printed list does, but look a bit closer and you will find lots of 'hidden' benefits:

- You can check the reading list without having your printed list to hand.
- The items will be linked to the catalogue – ironing out any mistakes or difficulties you might otherwise face (as discussed earlier in this chapter).
- You will be able to check immediately whether books are in stock, and make reservations online as required.
- If the full text is available, this will also be immediately accessible via a link.
- You will be able to check all this out at home or at work, saving you a lot of time and hassle, and enabling you to get on with your studies.

## 6.3 Reading round the subject

There will be other times when you don't have details of specific books to read. Sometimes, for an assignment there are a few key books that everyone needs to read, but then you are asked to apply the knowledge you've learned to a particular client group, or condition, relevant to the area in which you are working, or a area of your own choosing. You may, for example, be asked to look at management of patients with Chronic Obstructive Pulmonary Disease.

In this instance, you will be asking 'What books has the library got on this subject?' and the way to ask that is by doing a Subject or Keyword search. If you go back to the Search screen of the catalogue, you can now ignore the Author and Title search boxes and look instead for one called Keyword or Subject.

Again, try to keep it simple. Typing your whole essay title – *Management of Patients with Chronic Obstructive Pulmonary Disease* – into the box won't produce results. It is too specific, and will only work if there is an exact match to these words in this particular order. Instead, go for a more general term such as *Lung Diseases*, and you should immediately get some hits. You can also combine terms: *Mental Health* and *Adolescents*; *Stroke* and *Speech Therapy*; *Diet* and *Cancer*.

When you search for a subject in this way you are likely to get a greater number of results than when you search for a specific book by author and title. You can usually go through the list quite quickly and select the titles that seem to be the most relevant. You will often find that there is also a facility to sort the list in various ways. Sorting by date, with the most recent first, is often the most useful method. In the health professions things change rapidly and we are always seeking the most recent information.

You will need to note whether the book is available and, if so, its shelf-mark so that you can find it.

### Searching by class number

This is another potentially useful way of finding books on a particular subject. Once you have found the relevant class number(s) for the subject, many library catalogues will allow you to search for other books at this class number.

If you have exhausted the other channels, it is well worth giving this strategy a try – it is very likely to come up with some useful extra titles.

## 6.4 What if books are 'not available'?

If the book is in stock but not immediately available, either because it is on loan to another student or because it is held in another library, you will need to 'request' or 'reserve' it – see the next section.

If it is not in the library at all, it may be possible to obtain it from another library through the 'Interlibrary Loans' scheme. We look at Interlibrary Loans later in this chapter.

Whether or not you decide to place an Interlibrary Loan, please do let the library staff know that the book you require is not available. It is more than likely that this is the first they will have heard about the book being required reading, and – subject to funds being available – you can expect immediate action to add the item to stock. But bear in mind that delivery of stock may take some weeks from the library placing its order.

**When all the books have flown... and you're running out of time**

As we said at the beginning of this chapter, sometimes there are just not enough books to go round, and there will be occasions – hopefully not too many – where you feel defeated on every front when trying to obtain books for your studies.

Things are rarely as bad as they seem, and in this section we suggest a few strategies you could follow if the books you want are proving really elusive.

■ **Make reference and 'overnight' collections work for you**
Many libraries keep copies of books in high demand as 'reference only' or 'overnight loan' only. They will often transfer books to such collections, and if you feel your needs have been overlooked and could benefit in this way, then do let the library know.

■ **Use chapters in more general books**
If you cannot find a book on asthma, try widening your search a little. There may be an excellent section in a book on respiratory disorders.

There are also many wide-ranging general textbooks which contain excellent chapters on specific topics. *Nursing practice: hospital and home* (Alexander, Fawcett and Runciman 2006), for instance, has a wealth of useful chapters ranging from giving injections and taking blood pressure, to manual handling and infection control.

■ **Is the publication available on the web?**
Do remember that many official and institutional publications are published on the Internet. Recent reports from the Department of Health or Royal College of Nursing, for instance, are almost always available on the Internet. So you may not even have to chase that book after all! We talk in more detail in Chapter 8 about e-books and virtual publications.

# 6.5 Reservations

You can normally do this from the catalogue, even if you are working at home. Library staff will then work to satisfy your request and you will be informed when the book is ready for you to collect.

Don't be shy about making reservations – if you just wait patiently for the book to come back, other students will simply beat you to it and you may never get the book you want. Different libraries have different ways of dealing with reserved books. In some systems, the library, while not permitting renewals, will wait for the book to be returned – possibly meaning a wait to the end of the initial loan period. Other libraries are more pro-active and operate a 'recall' system. This means the current borrower is notified that someone else is waiting for it and given a reduced time in which to return the book.

## 6.6 Interlibrary loans

Sometimes, the book you want simply isn't in your library's stock. Talk to a librarian – perhaps a subject librarian who specialises in health – who may be able to suggest a good alternative that is in stock.

Another possibility is that your book could be obtained for you on interlibrary loan (ILL). The interlibrary loan service is just what it says – one library lending to another. Many libraries belong to local cooperative ILL schemes and may be able to locate your book this way. Another possibility is the British Library Document Supply Centre, which holds and loans over 3 million books.

The British Library service is not free and your library will have a policy on eligibility for loans from this source. It may be that undergraduates are only entitled to a limited number of loans, or that they can only be obtained for final year dissertations, or that a tutor's signature is required – but it is certainly worth asking if you feel that a book is particularly important to you.

## 6.7 Books or journal articles?

As a student you will need to access not just books but journal articles. In Chapter 10 we discuss the reasons for this, and the best techniques to use (which are rather different from those we recommend for books in Chapters 6 and 7).

As journal articles are such important sources of information, sooner or later your tutor will expect you to be able to make effective use of them. And your first encounter may be through a reading list.

Many reading lists comprise solely book titles. However, some tutors will add journal articles. At first sight you may think these are also books, as they will begin with an author and title. But, if towards the end you can spot a series of numbers, including a year, volume number, page numbers etc., then you can be reasonably certain the reference is to a journal article.

Tracking these down involves a whole new set of skills; we will look at this in Chapter 12.

**Reference**

Alexander, M., Fawcett, J. and Runciman, P. (eds.) (2006) *Nursing practice: hospital and home*. Edinburgh: Churchill Livingstone.

## Top tips

- Be prepared to reserve books not immediately available.
- Don't depend on only one or two books and don't necessarily go for exactly the same books as other students. Most lecturers will tell you that it makes for much livelier seminars if students have ideas to contribute from different sources.
- Consider using chapters from more general books
- Don't necessarily expect to keep a book for a long period. It may be recalled or you may not be able to renew it. Make good use of it while you've got it. Pick the most important chapters or pages to concentrate on.
- Be prepared to return books promptly when they are due and don't let fines mount up. Library fines are a complete waste of money and easily avoided if you keep a note of due dates and know how to renew.

## 6.8 Buying books

For a hard-up student, buying all the books you might like to own for your course is never going to be a realistic option. Nor would it be expected of you when you have the resources of an academic library at your disposal. However, there may well be one or two key texts that are going to be useful throughout your course and it's well worth investing in these.

On your reading list you will usually find that some books have been identified as 'Essential' or 'Mandatory' reading, and you would be well advised to purchase one or more of these. Some libraries deliberately adopt the approach of not buying multiple copies of books considered essential reading, on the grounds that students are expected to buy these and this frees up book funds to buy a much wider range of books to meet everyone's needs.

Don't rush into buying – it may well be that there are several similar books for you to choose from and that the style of one might suit your way of learning better than the others. You may even be able to get together with friends so that instead of all owning the same book, you own a range of books between you that you agree to share. Try to at least have a look at the various possible books, either in the library or a bookshop, before making a purchase.

Most academic institutions will have their own bookshops, either on campus or very near. University bookshops will aim to stock all the books on reading lists and will be able to order for you items not currently in stock. Major bookshops such as Borders or Waterstones also carry popular textbooks and will order for you. Other popular choices for buying textbooks are Internet booksellers such as Amazon, Blackwells and Waterstones. Don't forget to allow for the cost of delivery and note what they say about availability – items not in stock can sometimes take a long time to arrive.

### Buying second-hand

Buying second-hand books is a tempting option and your library or Students' Union may very well have a scheme for buying books from other students. You will also sometimes see second-hand books advertised for sale on campus notice boards. You could very well pick up a real bargain.

Do remember though, to check on the edition you are buying. If you are investing in a book, it should be the latest edition. Books are often advertised as being 'in very good condition', but it's more important that the book be up-to-date than that it isn't dog-eared. Condition can be important too – it is very irritating to find that a previous owner has underlined passages or coloured in diagrams. You can also buy second-hand from Amazon, but there are risks in buying unseen. You can, however, return books that aren't in satisfactory condition.

And of course, you can always sell the books on once you've finished with them!

# CHAPTER 7

# Using books

> ## In this chapter
>
> - Evaluating books
> - Which bits to use?
> - Keeping records
> - Referencing books

## 7.1 Evaluating books

If you can't judge a book by its cover – then how can you?

If a book is on a reading list, then it has been recommended by your tutor and you should have no problems in using it. To a lesser extent, the fact that a book is held in your institution's library is also a good indication. Libraries can't afford to buy everything so selection by quality goes on. When you find books by your own endeavours you need some ways of judging their value and usefulness. Ask yourself:

- **Who wrote or edited this book?** The title page will normally indicate the professional standing of the authors or editors. Are they academics from reputable institutions, working in relevant fields to your subject area? Are they clinicians working in a health context that you recognise (a hospital, community setting etc.)? Publishers are normally anxious to publicise the credentials of their authors. If no mention is made of the professional or academic standing of the authors or editors, you should ask yourself why not?
- **When was the book written?** Nursing and other health disciplines change rapidly in the light of ongoing research and changing social factors. A book written twenty years ago, however highly regarded at the time, should be treated with some caution today. As a very rough rule of thumb, for books on clinical procedures, you might like to think in terms of focusing initially only on material published in the last five years. Older material will be

more acceptable for areas where change is less rapid: psychology, child development and research techniques.

Always look for the most up-to-date material that you can find.

- **Is this the latest edition?** Try whenever possible to obtain the most recent edition. Books go into new editions precisely because of changes since the first edition. But bear in mind that changes are more significant in some areas than in others. Human anatomy and physiology won't have changed in five years, but surgical techniques may well have. Basing your essay on something that is currently regarded as 'unsafe practice' may earn you an automatic fail.

- **Who published the book?** Certain publishers are particularly noted for high-quality books in the fields of medicine and health, but many publishers will also publish excellent books in your disciplines as part of a general range. Watch out, however, for publishers with particular interests to promote. For example, a book or pamphlet on nutrition published by a body set up to promote a particular foodstuff (e.g. dairy products or meat) is unlikely to be completely unbiased. Similarly, books published by pharmaceutical companies or equipment manufacturers should be treated with caution.

- **Who is this book aimed at?** The publisher's 'blurb' on the back of the book will often tell you this. If at all possible, try to find books that are aimed at your professional group and that are at the right academic level for you. It's very off-putting to struggle with a book that's aimed at senior medical staff when you're a first-year student nurse.

Some books won't meet these standards relating to academic or professional authorship, but can still be very valuable to you. There are books written by individuals, or carers of individuals, who have the very illnesses or conditions that you are studying.

For example, Mark Haddon's very entertaining novel *The curious incident of the dog in the night-time* gives an insight into the mind of an autistic boy. John Bayley's *Iris* is a harrowing autobiographical account of his brilliant wife's decline into Alzheimer's disease. Books of this kind can help you to understand what it feels like to be the patient or carer, and give you great insight into how patients wish to be treated. However, they are not academic sources and should not form the basis of an academic assignment.

## 7.2 Which bits should you use?

However important a textbook seems to be, it's rare that you would be expected to read the whole book at once. Some major health texts cover almost everything you might be expected to learn at undergraduate level and are intended for students to dip into and select from as the need arises. An example for general adult nursing would be *The Royal Marsden Hospital manual of clinical nursing procedures*. The trick is to learn how to pick some key pieces of information from them.

There are two tools to help you here: the contents page and the index.

### Contents page

The contents page will appear before the main text and will give you a good idea of how the book is structured and what each chapter is intended to cover. You may well find that all you need at the moment is contained within one chapter that you can go straight to.

### Index

The index will appear at the back of the book, after the main text, and is an alphabetical listing of all the terms that have been used in the book and the pages on which they have been used. You may be looking for information that has been scattered throughout the book and the index will show you where to find it. Look out for page numbers in bold type, which will be an indication of the most important pages on the subject you are looking for.

## 7.3 Keeping a record

When surrounded by piles of useful books and constantly dipping into several of them for useful facts or good quotes to support your argument, it's very easy to get carried away and then forget which book you had this vital information from.

If you've written in your assignment 'there was a drop of 36% in MRSA cases in England between 2007 and 2008' and then aren't able to reference the source of this little gem, then you aren't going to be able to use it, and your assignment – along with your grade – is going to suffer. So every time you use a fact or a quote from a written source – *make a note of where it came from!* This doesn't need to be a very sophisticated note at this stage – you can work on your bibliography more when you've finished writing. A little note – Alexander, p. 216 – will do at this stage, as long as you know what this refers to.

For students using Microsoft Word to word-process their assignment, there is a very simple method of capturing your references as you go along. If you go to Insert on your toolbar, then select Reference and then Footnote, it will take you to the bottom of the page. There you can type in your quick reference and your references will appear in a numbered list, which you can amend later if necessary.

This is a very convenient way of keeping records for yourself. But you do need to be aware that this is unlikely to be an acceptable way of referencing for your completed assignment – and most certainly not if your institution follows the Harvard referencing conventions – see Chapter 4. Specific information about how to reference books and/or chapters follows next in this chapter.

## 7.4 How to reference books (and chapters)

As we said in Chapter 4, within the text of your assignment you need to cite your sources as you go. In the Harvard system of referencing, the citation takes the format 'author' and 'year'. So if you quote from the first example below you will insert: (Genders 2006, p. 19). That is the simple bit. How you write the full reference at the end of your assignment is where you have to be very careful to provide the correct information in the correct format.

Whenever possible, you should take your information from the title page – a prominent page at the start of the book which states the title and author of the book – or the back of the title page (the copyright page) which will normally give you details of the publisher, date of publication, edition and so on – rather than the cover or anywhere else.

A basic reference needs the following information:

- Name (surname first, then initials) of the author or editor
- Date (year) that the book was published (in round brackets)
- Title of the book, and subtitle if there is one (in italics)
- Number of the edition, unless it is the first edition
- Place of publication
- Name of the publisher

There are also conventions about the use of punctuation – follow the form of punctuation used in the examples below.

**Book with single author**
Genders, N. (2006) *Fundamental aspects of complementary therapies for health care professionals*. London: Quay Books.

**Books with editors**
If a book is edited rather than entirely written by one or more people, you should indicate this with (ed.) or (eds.)

Tremayne, P. and Parboteah, S. (eds.) (2006) *Fundamental aspects of adult nursing procedures*. London: Quay Books.

**Referencing a chapter**
If you have used a single chapter with a named author from an edited book you will need to reference both the chapter and also the book in which it appears.

Anthony, D. (2005) 'Using information technology', in Maslin-Prothero, S. (ed.) *Baillière's study skills for nurses and midwives*, 3rd ed. Edinburgh: Baillière Tindall.

**More than three authors or editors**
If a book has more than three authors, then there is no need to list them all. Just give the name of the first author, followed by '*et al.*', which means 'and others'.

Nicol, M. *et al.* (2008) *Essential nursing skills*, 3rd ed. Edinburgh: Mosby.

**Corporate authors**
Sometimes a publication has no individual named authors but has been produced by a body of people, known as a 'corporate author'. In this case you can only name the body that has produced it.

National Forensic Nurses' Research and Development Group (ed.) (2007) *Forensic mental health nursing: forensic aspects of acute care*. London: Quay Books.

**Government publications**

Government publications often have no named authors and in this case the country and the department that produced the document are regarded as the authors.

Great Britain. Department of Health (2008) *Reference guide to the Mental Health Act*. London: TSO.

# Top tips

- Record all the details you will need for referencing, including the page numbers of any specific quotes you will use, while you have the book in your possession.
- Photocopy the important pages. Although you need to be aware of copyright issues, copyright law does allow for some copying under what is known as 'fair dealing' and this is generally regarded as one chapter or up to 5% of the book. Never exceed this.
- Consider making notes to avoid copying costs

# E-books

## 8.1 E-books

There is much talk about whether the traditional book has a future – won't the e-book take its place? As yet there is a little sign of this happening, but just as e-journals have transformed that sector, it may be that a similar revolution will take place in the world of books. However, the number of e-books in the nursing and health care sector is very limited indeed.

Nevertheless, some e-books are available. And there are clear potential benefits. If you are working from home, you will no longer to need to travel to your library to pick up your next piece of reading. In addition, online availability should mean an end to the frustration of being beaten to the bookshelf by your colleagues, or having to wait your turn for reserved books.

Your university catalogue will make it clear when titles are available in e-book format. Please note that these cannot always be consulted just like any other document on the Internet. It all depends on the agreement made between your library and the supplier. Under some arrangements you will need to 'book' time to consult the e-book; and if someone else is already reading it, you will have to wait your turn.

## 8.2 Virtual publications

What, you may be wondering, is the difference between e-books and virtual books? In general, for the user, absolutely none! But it seems useful to make a distinction here between 'e-books' promoted by publishers and libraries – these tend to be standard student texts, published on a commercial basis – and the vast range of official reports and guidelines which are available on the web, often in PDF form. In this book we use the term 'virtual publications' to refer to the latter.

Once aware that a certain amount of material is available on the web, students quickly become accustomed to searching across the web for particular enquiries. The actual nature and quality of the 'hits' varies enormously. We look in more detail at this quality issue in Chapter 13. What we focus on here is the range of high-quality publications that can be accessed via the web.

A significant proportion of essential and recommended reading for nursing and health students is published by government and it is worth bearing this in mind when looking for titles on your reading list. Outlined below are some of the more important sources of virtual publications that will be relevant to you.

When you see these in a reading list, they will look just like any other title. All are likely to be referred to as 'publications' and referenced with authors and titles, so you might not immediately think to look on the web to find the full text. Although librarians will do their best to ensure that the library catalogue will contain links to all these virtual publications, some will inevitably escape their attention.

- **Department of Health reports and other publications**
  Health and social care reports – usually published by the Department of Health, but quite often by other departments such as the Department for Children, Schools and Families – are invariably published on the web nowadays. Indeed, quite frequently, they are now only available on the Internet.

  As an example, you will find all the National Service Framework publications available on the Department's website (Figure 8.1).
- **Royal College of Nursing (RCN)**
  Many professional bodies now see electronic publications as the primary way of making information available. As you might expect, a full range of such publications can be accessed on the RCN website (http://www.rcn.org.uk/), covering topics from infection control to informed consent.
- **Nursing and Midwifery Council (NMC)**
  A further example of a professional body which makes its publications freely available over the Internet. The Code, which outlines standards of conduct, performance and ethics for nurses and midwives, and which will certainly be required reading on your course, is one of the key documents available from the NMC website: http://www.nmc-uk.org/.

**Figure 8.1** *National Service Framework for Renal Services*: full text publication available online free via the Department of Health website : http://www.dh.gov. uk/.

- **Health authorities: medical policies, codes etc**.
  All health authorities will have published policies covering areas such as prescribing, infection control etc. In the past these would have been available in printed form, but nowadays they are usually only in 'virtual format'. Sadly, many of these tend to be published in authorities' intranets, which means they are only available to local staff. However, if you work or are on placement at an NHS hospital, you will be able to see these documents for yourself.

  A limited number are now being published on the Internet, and with implementation of the Freedom of Information Act, it seems reasonable to expect that more will become available in the future.

  An example is the Leicestershire Medicines Code, which can be seen on the website of the Leicestershire Strategy Medicines Group: http://www. lmsg.nhs.uk/.

## How to reference an e-book or virtual publication

If you have used an e-book you will need to reference it in much the same way as a printed book, but you will need some additional information to show where and when you accessed it.

*Example*:
Fry, S. and Johnstone, M.-J. (2002) *Ethics in nursing practice*, 2nd ed. Blackwell. [Online]. Available at: http://www.library.nhs.uk/booksandjournals/ebooks/ [Accessed: 23/09/08].

# CHAPTER 9

# Other media: DVDs, CDs, audiocassettes etc.

**In this chapter**

- Physical formats
- Commercial products
- Off-air recordings

## 9.1 Physical formats

As well as books and printed journals, most libraries carry a range of other materials, such as DVDs, CDs, audiocassettes and videotapes – often collectively referred to as 'media'. These may be kept in one or more separate sequences or they may be shelved alongside books on the same subject, depending on the policy of your library.

Sometimes you may search your library catalogue using a subject or keyword search and find that, as well as a number of books on the subject, the library holds some DVDs. Don't disregard these. They can be a very useful addition to the available information.

DVD has now overtaken videotape as the most used format, so we will use the term DVD. However, your library may still hold material in videotape format and have viewing facilities, even if you can no longer view videos at home.

DVDs held in library collections fall into two main types – commercial products, and off-air recordings.

## 9.2 Commercial products

These are DVDs produced and distributed by commercial companies for educational purposes in exactly the same way as publishers produce books. Examples include:

- Bates' visual guides to physical examination
- Acland's DVD atlas of human anatomy

There is really nothing special about DVDs of this sort. They are simply visual representations of the same sort of information that you might find expressed in a book. You should therefore treat them in exactly the same way.
Ask yourself:

- Who created this information?
- For what purpose?
- Who is it intended for?
- When was it created – is the information still current?

In particular, watch out for particular bias on the part of the producer. If a DVD on depression is produced by a drug company, then it is unlikely to be completely neutral about the effectiveness of a drug treatment. A DVD on the effects of cholesterol on the heart produced by a food company promoting dairy products is unlikely to be completely neutral, fair and unbiased.
Use DVDs of this sort as an additional resource but bring your critical faculties to bear on them – ask yourself constantly what are the values and motives of the people who create these materials.
If you are a person who learns best from seeing something expressed in a visual way, you might find that watching DVDs fixes complex information in your mind much more effectively than many hours of book reading, so it would be well worth while to seek them out.

## 9.3 Off-air recordings

'Off-air recording' means a television or radio programme which has been recorded onto DVD to add to library stock and use as an educational resource.

Health in its many aspects is a matter of great concern to the general public and as such there are endless television programmes about it. Hardly a week goes by without a major health documentary on television.

It is quite legitimate to refer in your assignment to factual or documentary programmes, whether from library stock or viewed live, or from feature films, provided you keep some things in mind:

- Bring your critical faculties to bear – you need to ask yourself just the same kinds of questions as for books: who created the programme and why? Who is it intended for? When was the programme made – is it still current? Is it fair and balanced in its treatment of the subject or does it present a particular point of view?

- Remember that although you wish to make use of such programmes for educational purposes, they have been created mainly for entertainment value. You should treat them with caution but they can still be useful to you. Very often the titles of television documentaries are sensational and quite shocking, for deliberate effect on the public.

  You as a health professional – or a health professional in training – should be able to look beyond the title. 'The boy whose skin fell off' is a very dramatic title, but it was in fact a serious documentary about a young man with a rare genetic disorder which also raised issues about death and dying, end of life care and bereavement. 'Dana: the eight year old anorexic' covered issues relating to child psychology, parental attitudes and treatment options.

- Such programmes often feature a high-profile celebrity in order to appeal to the public. 'The secret life of the manic depressive' was Stephen Fry's exploration of what it is like to live with bipolar disorder. You need to be able to look beyond celebrity and judge the programme on its merits.

- Television or radio programmes, or films, of this type can be immensely helpful in showing the realities of life with serious health problems. Often one such programme, if well made, will tell you more than any textbook about what it feels like. They do often tend to focus on one individual's experiences, so they may not be completely balanced in their approach. This is just something you need to keep in mind.

- You need a balanced approach. Use a television programme or a film as an illustration of an argument, not as a basis for your whole assignment. If you have used a good range of books, journal articles and websites then you can also include a television programme, but you can't use one as a substitute for reading academic sources.

If you have mentioned a programme or film in your writing then you must reference it. If you watched something which increased your knowledge and understanding of your subject, but you didn't directly refer to it in your assignment, then put it into a bibliography.

## How to reference a DVD, video or television programme

Your reference should include as much of the following information as is available:

- title of DVD (or film or programme)
- year of publication (or distribution)
- originator (e.g. director)
- indication of medium, e.g. [DVD] or [Videocassette]
- place of publication (or distribution)
- publisher (or distributor)

*Example*:
*Communicating with children and families* (2006) [DVD] Philadelphia: Lippincott Williams & Wilkins.

To reference a television programme you should also include the channel, the date and time and any episode number (if the programme is part of a series).

*Example*:
*Tony Robinson: me and my mum* (2006) [TV] Channel 4. 27 March. 21.00 hrs.

# PART III

# Journal articles

# CHAPTER 10

# Journals

## In this chapter

- What are journals?
- Why are journals important?
- Types of journal
- How to evaluate a journal
- Online journals
- How to search journals
- How to reference journal articles

## 10.1  What are journals?

Journals, also known as 'serials' or 'periodicals', are publications which are issued on a regular basis. Some, such as *Nursing Times*, are published weekly; many others, *Emergency Nurse* for instance, appear monthly. Some titles are published even less regularly. Examples are *European Journal of Palliative Care*, which appears bi-monthly, and *Annual Review of Nursing Research*, which, as you might expect, comes out once a year.

Typically journals focus on a particular subject area, and contain a range of articles and features written by different people. Some, such as *Nursing Times* or *Nursing Standard*, cover all branches of nursing.

Not so long ago journals were only available as printed products, but recent years have seen rapid advances in electronic publishing of journals. Indeed, some journals, such as *Special Children* or *Mental Health Nursing*, are now *only* available online. This may mean that many students today rarely handle a printed journal and are only aware of articles as virtual documents on the Internet.

It can be difficult to understand the difference between a journal article and other material you read on the web. For this reason it is probably worth making an effort to visit your library and take time to handle printed copies and become familiar with the format. This could bring extra benefits. Regular reading of *Nursing Standard* will be a great help in keeping up to date with the latest developments in nursing and health care.

## 10.2 Why are journals important?

Journals are perhaps the most important way of tracking down information and keeping abreast of the latest research. They are important because they allow articles to be published quickly, and the information made available to the public much sooner than would be the case if they had to wait for a book to be published.

As a student you will soon discover that:

■ There is not a book for every subject you want to study
■ Some books which look relevant will actually be out of date
■ It is virtually impossible for even brand new books to be 100% up to date because of the time they take to be written, printed and published. It can easily be a year, and often more, between conception and appearing in the bookshop.

For all these reasons, journals have become a very important and widely recognised means of communication for new ideas and new research among academic and professional workers.

## 10.3 Types of journal

Journals are published by a range of different types of organisations and for a range of different purposes. Broadly speaking they fall in to three or four major categories: scholarly, trade and professional, and popular.

■ **Scholarly** journals, such as *Journal of Advanced Perioperative Care*, are the most important type for students. They are intended for an audience already knowledgeable about the subject. They are 'peer-reviewed' (or 'refereed'), which means that the content has been carefully scrutinised by experts in the subject before publication. Peer-reviewed journals will make

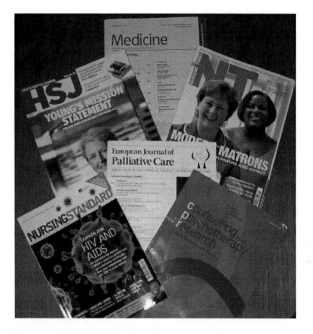

**Figure 10.1** Examples of nursing-related journals.

this clear in their introduction, and will almost certainly name their editorial board. The journal may also outline its editorial policy and the criteria used for assessing articles before publishing them.

For most purposes, and certainly for any research in connection with evidence-based practice, it is usually advisable to make sure that a significant number of your references are from scholarly journals.

- **Professional and trade** journals, such as *Nursing Standard* and *Nursing Times*, are aimed at people working in the area. Although aimed at people particularly knowledgeable about the subject, their editorial policies and publishing criteria may vary considerably.
- **Popular** journals – usually called magazines – are intended for a general audience, with no specialist knowledge in the area. Examples are *Top Santé* or *Zest*. Profit is the key motive for publishing popular journals.

## 10.4 Evaluating journals

After reading the previous section, your next question might well be – which journals can I safely use? How can I be sure that I am using a scholarly journal? This section provides some key criteria for evaluating individual journals.

- **Editors**
  Who sits on the journal's editorial board? Are they academics from reputable institutions or clinicians working in an appropriate area? This information usually appears at the front of the journal, often inside the front cover.
- **Authors**
  What is known about the authors of the articles? Are they experts in their fields? How much information is given about their background? This information is usually given at the start of the article.
- **Purpose of the articles**
  Do the articles set out to provide information about new research? Some articles may have other aims – e.g. to provide a general overview of a subject (literature review). In less scholarly journals the aim may be persuade people of a certain point of view.
- **Bibliographies**
  All articles should carry a list of references (bibliography).
- **Are the lists reasonably comprehensive?**
  When where the articles published? Are they sufficiently current?
- **Readership**
  What is the intended readership? There will be clues in the writer's use of language. Articles aimed at the general public will tend to avoid technical terms, and where used, will make an effort to explain them. If aimed at fellow professionals, there will be no such concessions and the article will use the normal language and vocabulary shared by practitioners in that field.

## 10.5 Online journals

A large number of nursing and health journals are now available electronically, and students or NHS workers will be able to access some of these at home, at work or at their learning institution. The exact range of journals available for access will vary from institution to institution.

If you have an NHS Athens login, you can access over 1,500 online journals through the NLH website. A full list of journals available nationally is available at http://journals.library.nhs.uk/.

Additional titles might be available through local NHS libraries.

University students will also be able to access a wide range of journals online through their own institutional subscriptions. The exact range of available journals will vary from institution to institution, as will the exact method of gaining access. Often (but not always) an Athens password will be required.

Many university websites offer a special 'e-Journals' index page. This will take the user directly to the available resource.

### Free access

It is worth noting that some articles can currently be accessed in full text online at no charge by anyone who wishes to. PubMed and Stanford University's HighWire Press, both based in America, provide full details of free sites on their websites.

Neither claims to be a comprehensive list: both are limited to journals with which those organisations have some form of agreement. Other journals may also be available, and some – such as *Nursing Standard* – will be particularly familiar to nursing students. This title can be accessed free, but you will need first to register on the journal's website.

## 10.6 Print journals

University and health libraries have large holdings of journals in print format, often dating back many years. Current trends are for print subscriptions to be cancelled in favour of online access, but existing holdings should remain accessible for many years to come.

Print journals are almost always available for use in library only (i.e. borrowing for use elsewhere is not permitted), so a visit to the holding library will be necessary to see the article. However, it is usually possible to take photocopies of articles – provided you stay within copyright law.

Current UK law permits individuals to make a single copy of a reasonable proportion of a journal for their own private study or research for non-commercial purposes. A 'reasonable proportion' in terms of journals is generally understood to mean one article in a single issue of the periodical. You should also not make more than one copy of the article, and you also need to be satisfied that no fellow student or worker has made, or intends to make, a copy of the same article for the same purpose.

If you are willing to travel to other locations, it is possible that you could check the library catalogues of other institutions online to find out what resources might be available to you. Students of universities which belong to the SCONUL Access scheme (see Chapter 1) will be best placed to take advantage of holdings at other institutions. Arrangements for access and copying will vary, so it is always best to phone the library of the institution you wish to visit before setting out.

Even if you cannot enrol for SCONUL Access (whether because of your status, the status of your home institution, or the status of the institution you wish to visit), it is always worth contacting the librarian where the journal is held, as there may be other arrangements available to help you.

## 10.7 Searching journals

There are a number of important questions you might want to ask before beginning a search for journal articles. For example: Which journals should I be using? How can I get access to the content of specific articles?

In practice, you will find you can in most cases simply skate over these questions. One of the great advances in information in recent years has been the development of databases which enable you to search across hundreds of journals simultaneously. And if you begin your search using quality databases such as BNI (British Nursing Index) or CINAHL, the articles you find should be of the scholarly standard you require.

Searching through databases will also often lead you straight to the content of specific articles (but not always!).

As database searching requires a whole new set of skills, we have devoted the whole of Chapters 11 and 12 to this subject.

## 10.8 How to reference journal articles

This is covered in detail in Section 12.7 after we have looked at the issues around identifying specific articles by using databases.

# CHAPTER 11

# Databases

> ## In this chapter
>
> - What is a database?
> - Access to databases
> - Choosing a database
> - Core databases

## 11.1 What is a database?

A database is any collection of information held electronically in such a way that it can be searched for by any of its component parts or 'fields'.

Databases don't have to be about technical and professional matters. For instance, you could set up your own database by gathering together all the contact details of friends and family and enter them into a product such as Microsoft Access. You could then search for everyone who has a birthday during May, or all friends who live in your area, or produce a list of everyone you want to send a Christmas card to.

When librarians talk about databases they usually mean electronic records of references to journal articles. Such a database would normally contain the details of articles from many different journals. There are many databases in the area of nursing and health care. Some hold details of articles from just a few hundred journals and some from several thousand – depending on the breadth of their coverage. British Nursing Index, for instance, contains 75,000 records dating back to 1985, with a further 9,000 added each year.

You would normally expect to find that the information held includes:

- title of the article
- author(s) of the article

- title of the journal in which the article appeared
- volume number, part (or issue) number and page numbers relating to where the article was published
- date the issue was published (usually just the year)
- some terms to describe the subject of the article

These sets of information are called fields. For instance, you will often see references to 'title field' or 'author field'.

In addition to these fields, there will frequently also be an 'abstract', or short summary, of the article. With luck you will also find a link which takes you to the full text of the article.

### Searching

In the same way that you could search your personal database for everyone who has a birthday next month, or look for the email address of one particular friend, you can search a database of journal articles just as selectively. So you can search for articles on a particular subject – as broad or as narrow as you wish; or you could look for articles by a particular author; or track down an article when you know its title but nothing else.

## 11.2 Access to databases

Databases are constantly being updated to include the very latest articles. They are very expensive to produce and for this reason have to be paid for by their users. As a student, you will find that your university has paid for you to have access to a range of appropriate databases.

Because of the high costs involved, it is unlikely that you will have access to every possible database, but you should find a selection of the most useful ones for your subject area available to you from your library's website. Another consequence of the high cost is that suppliers need to verify that only those people whose institutions have paid for them to use the database can do so. For this reason, you will be asked to give a username and password – normally Athens. There is more information about Athens accounts in Chapter 3.

## 11.3 Choosing a database

There are many databases that are relevant and useful to students of health subjects. Some, but not necessarily all, of them will be available to you via your university website. Visit the website and check what you can use. Most are also available via the National Library of Health – see Chapter 17.

You may find it confusing that there are so many to choose from. It is tempting to get to know just one and then always use the same one, but it will be a great help to you in finding information if you can choose the most appropriate database for the topic you are looking at. To get the best information you may need to look at more than one database. Sometimes you are offered the option of searching more than one database at a time, which is a really quick and efficient way to search.

At the end of this chapter we provide an overview of the main databases that may be available to you and describe some of their key features – subject coverage, number of journals indexed, time span covered, additional features – to help you to decide which to use. We have picked 14 that in our experience are most relevant to nursing students.

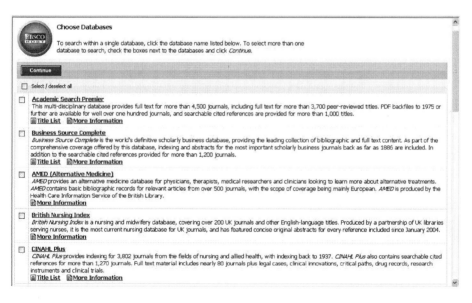

**Figure 11.1** The 'Choose database' page on the EBSCO website.

### Multi-searching

If nursing databases are new to you, even the limited range of 14 databases that we have identified may seem a little intimidating. But do not abandon hope just yet! Many students will find they can save worry, effort and, perhaps most importantly, time by being able to search several databases simultaneously.

If your university subscribes to BNI and CINAHL through EBSCO not only will you be able to search the two simultaneously, but you will also be able to include AMED, PsycINFO and Medline (Figure 11.1).

An NHS Athens account will give you access to a range of databases through NLH Search 2.0, which offers a single interface.

## 11.4 Core databases

### Nursing databases

*BNI – British Nursing Index*

This is the database most targeted to the needs of UK nursing students. It indexes over 200 UK and other English language journals and really does have something for everyone, as it covers all aspects of nursing at every level, from student to experienced specialist practitioner. It is compiled by librarians working at Bournemouth University, Poole Hospital NHS Trust, the Royal College of Nursing and Salisbury NHS Foundation Trust and based on the journals held in their libraries. From 2004 onwards there is an abstract to accompany every reference, but not always for older references.

It's hard now to imagine life without BNI, as it has become an essential tool for nursing and midwifery students. But a couple of notes of caution:

- Sometimes students are asked to look at examples of UK practice and think that they can be sure of this from BNI – but BNI indexes journals in English from around the world, so you would need to look carefully at the journal to establish that it is actually British.
- Don't depend too heavily on BNI and overlook some of the other excellent databases listed here.

*CINAHL – Cumulative Index to Nursing and Allied Health Literature*

CINAHL is a US database of references to articles on nursing and allied health from journals published around the world from 1982 onwards, many with abstracts. As well as a very thorough coverage of nursing journals, the allied health coverage includes: audiology, dental hygiene, medical/laboratory technology, nutrition and dietetics, occupational therapy, physical therapy and rehabilitation, radiology technology, and speech and language pathology.

For most nursing topics, using both BNI and CINAHL would give you a sufficiently thorough search.

*HMIC – Health Management Information Consortium*

The Health Management Information Consortium that gives this database its name consists of the Library and Information Services of the Department of Health and the Information and Library Service of the King's Fund. (The King's Fund is an independent charity that helps to develop health policy and effective services.)

The HMIC database covers all aspects of health management and policy, especially relating to the NHS in Britain, including public health, nursing and primary care, mental health, medical equipment and supplies, medicines safety, environment health and social services. As well as journal articles it includes other items from these two libraries and is particularly good for government publications in these areas, including many that are difficult to find elsewhere. Coverage goes back to 1983.

### Specialist databases

While BNI, CINAHL and HMIC provide good general nursing coverage, many students will have a strong interest in particular areas of health, such as care of elderly or young people. There are a number of important databases covering these areas.

*AgeInfo*

The AgeInfo database is produced by the Centre for Policy on Ageing, an organisation concerned with all the needs of older age people. The database is based on material held in the CPA's reference library, which has books, journals and reports on social, behavioural and health aspects of older age. The main database has over 40,000 books, journal articles and reports.

### AMED – Allied and Complementary Medicine Database

AMED is produced by the Health Care Information Service of the British Library. It covers several different subject areas, with different time spans:

- Complementary medicine, from 1985 onwards
- Professions allied to medicine: physiotherapy, occupational therapy, rehabilitation, podiatry, from 1985 onwards
- Palliative care, from 1997 onwards
- Speech and language therapy, from 1999 onwards

Almost 600 journals are indexed and many of these are not indexed in any other health or medical database. AMED is an essential database for students in many of the health disciplines and a really useful extra for nursing students.

### ASSIA – Applied Social Sciences Index and Abstracts

The name suggests that ASSIA is more for students of social sciences than health. However, its subject coverage is very extensive and includes such topics as: anxiety disorders, communication, ethnic studies, family, geriatrics, health, nursing, child abuse, NHS reforms and substance abuse. Over 500 journals are indexed, with records going back to 1987, and abstracts are also provided. This is definitely a database worth investigating for health students, especially for a topic with a social angle to it. If, for instance, you were exploring the relationship between ethnicity and health, or looking for information on child abuse, or the impact of unemployment on mental health, you could find very useful articles in ASSIA that you might not find from a more definitely medical or health-related database.

### ChildData

This database comes from the National Children's Bureau and is based on the holdings of their library, so contains more than just journal articles. NCB is concerned with all aspects of child welfare and this is reflected in the coverage of the ChildData database.

*Maternity and Infant Care*

This database, previously known as Midwifery and Infant Care, comes from MIDIRS – Midwives Information and Resources Service. It contains over 120,000 references to journal articles from over 550 English language journals from around the world relating to the midwifery profession, pregnancy, labour, birth, postnatal care, and neonatal care and the first year of an infant's life. The database also includes pamphlets, reports, newspaper articles and some chapters from books. Coverage is from the mid-1980s onwards.

*PsycINFO*

Produced by the American Psychological Association, PsycINFO indexes and abstracts professional and academic journals in the behavioural sciences and mental health and related disciplines including medicine, psychiatry, nursing, sociology, education, pharmacology, physiology and communications. Over 2,150 scholarly journals from around the world are indexed. It also includes some chapters from books in the English language.

Another database produced by the American Psychological Association, called PsycArticles, has the full text of articles from 60 scholarly journals mainly published by the APA. This one tends to be less widely available from UK academic libraries.

*Social Care Online*

Social Care Online is a free database produced by the Social Care Institute for Excellence (SCIE) and primarily intended for researchers, academics, practitioners and students of social work. It can also be useful for nursing or other health care students if you are looking at the more social aspects of a topic, or if you are looking at inter-professional working. The core subject areas include: families, children and young people; mental health and mental health care; groups and communities, including minority ethnic groups; physical and learning disabilities; health and health care; housing; psychology. Most of the material is from the UK and as well as journal articles the database includes government documents, reports and relevant websites.

### Medical databases

#### Medline and PubMed

The best known medical database is Medline, the US National Library of Medicine's database of 15 million references to journal articles in life sciences, especially medicine. You may find you only have access to PubMed, which is available free over the Internet

PubMed is basically Medline with some added bells and whistles. Medline is by far the major component, but PubMed also contains some extra material – probably of less interest to healthcare students – such as articles not yet indexed in Medline, or very old material. You can choose to search Medline only. PubMed includes links to sites where the full text may be available to you.

### Other general databases

There are also some general databases that you could use, which cover a wide range of subject matter, not just health or medicine. These can be excellent, but you need to be quite discriminating in your use of them. You should look very carefully at the references that you find to make sure that they do indeed relate to healthcare or nursing. You can make this easier by including 'nursing' or other health-related terms in your original search.

#### Scopus

Scopus is a huge database of 33 million records from 15,000 journals, plus many millions of quality web sources. It is designed for the use of researchers in scientific, technical, medical and social sciences disciplines. It offers basic or advanced searching and links to full text articles when they are available.

The sheer size of Scopus can be a problem, but is easily overcome if you select your search terms carefully. For example, a search for *communication* and *confidentiality* for the past five years brought up over a thousand articles, 665 of which were medical, 184 were engineering and only 95 were nursing. Searching for communication, confidentiality *and nursing* over the same period produced 80 results – a bit more manageable. You can also exclude anything other than a complete journal article, which again reduces the number of results and is more likely to give you what you need.

*Web of Knowledge*

Web of Knowledge is a group of databases on science, social sciences, arts and humanities, plus some conference proceedings. You can choose to search a single database or more than one at the same time. There are links to full text where it is available.

*Zetoc*

Zetoc is a general database which indexes 20,000 current research journals on a wide range of subjects held in the British Library from 1993 onwards. It also has 16,000 conference proceedings, but you can opt for journal articles only before you start to search. Because of the way the database is structured you can't use the useful combining features of AND, OR and NOT that you can in some other databases (see p. 82), but if you enter a string of terms into the search box Zetoc will assume you want articles containing all those terms. If you wanted articles on the role of sharps disposal in infection control, you can enter *infection sharps* and Zetoc will automatically combine them. As with Scopus, if you are looking for a health-related topic you may get a better result if you include *nursing* (or a similar term) as one of your search terms.

# CHAPTER 12

# Using databases

## In this chapter

- Using a database
- Search strategies
- Record keeping
- From reference to actual article
- Accessing articles in print
- Interlibrary loans
- How to reference journal articles
- Do get help

One thing that seems guaranteed to wind up the average student is the very topic we consider in this chapter – how to search databases effectively. Here we aim to reassure and give a range of advice on how to get the best results.

Perhaps the best advice we can give is in the final part of this chapter – do not be afraid to seek help. Learning to use a database is so much easier if you have a skilled and friendly human being to show you.

It is also worth remembering that databases are constantly being upgraded, and what works for you today may not work so well next week or next month. So once again the watchword has to be – ask for help from your library staff.

## 12.1 Using a database

If you look at even a few of the databases listed in Chapter 11, you will soon see that they all look a bit different and are searched in slightly different ways. But they all have one thing in common – search boxes where you enter the subjects about which you want information.

It's very easy to tell you what not to do: don't type your assignment title into the search box and hope that the database will magically find an article that will answer your essay question for you – because it won't. To get the best results from a database you need to go about your search in a carefully structured way.

Your library will probably have help guides to some of the most popular databases, either online (sometimes called 'Guide at the Side') or as a printed leaflet. In this chapter we offer some general advice to get you started.

Many databases give you the choice between a 'Basic' or 'Easy' search and an 'Advanced' search. The basic search will normally give you all the information you need to help with an assignment.

Databases usually offer you the option of searching for an author by name, for a specific title, or by subjects or keywords. Searching for an author can be very useful – if for instance you knew that there were excellent articles on deep vein thrombosis by someone called Autar you could find them easily by typing this name into the author box.

It's much more likely that you won't have such an easy starting point, but will just want to know what has been published on the topic you are studying. In this case you will need to choose 'Keywords' or 'Subject terms' to search for. You need to look carefully at your assignment topic and break it down into its component parts.

## 12.2 Search strategies

There are a number of aspects to consider if you want to get the best results from your search:

- identify concepts
- consider synonyms
- think of broader or narrower terms
- abbreviations – or spelled out
- combine concepts
- and, or, not?
- spelling – variants and errors
- truncation
- timescale
- descriptors

### Identify the main concepts of your topic

This means asking yourself which ideas are most important. If, for instance, you are writing an assignment on 'Causes and prevention of falls in the elderly' there are two main concepts here – *falls* and *elderly*. These are the terms for which you would search, and you can ignore all linking words – so you would type 'falls' in the search box, not 'causes of falls'. If your subject was 'Management of minor injuries in the community' your key concepts would be *'minor injuries'* and *'community'*. You might want to think of examples of minor injuries – perhaps *'broken wrist'*.

### Consider synonyms

A synonym is a word that has a meaning very similar to another word and which may be used as an alternative. So *elderly*, *aged* and *geriatric* are words of similar meaning which might be used as alternatives. *Adolescent* and *teenage* might be used as synonyms. To be sure you are finding all relevant articles you may need to search for several synonymous terms. It's useful to make a list before you start to search.

### Think of broader or narrower terms

Sometimes, a search will find very few articles. This may be because you have used a very specific search term. You may need to broaden your search more. For example, if *'asthma'* gives very few results, try *'respiratory disorders'*.

Alternatively, if a search finds far more articles than you want, you may need to narrow your search to a more specific term. If *'eating disorders'* finds far too many articles, try *'anorexia nervosa'*. Again, it can be useful to list these alternative terms before you start to search.

### Using abbreviations or spelling out in full

Abbreviations are part of the everyday language of health care. It's normal to speak of 'c diff' or 'MRSA'; 'COPD' or 'MS'. However, you may find that if you use these terms for your database search you don't get the results you are expecting and that you may do better if you spell terms out in full: *'Clostridium difficile'* or *'Chronic Obstructive Pulmonary Disorder'*. You may find it helpful to refer to a good medical dictionary if you are uncertain what the full term should be or how it is spelt.

### Combine concepts

Once you have identified your key concepts and decided which search terms to use, you can begin your search. You are looking for articles which cover all your concepts so you may need to combine them. Different databases have different ways of combining search terms.

Often you carry out your initial very general search, and then, depending on the number of results, you can go back and simply add an extra term to the search box and search again. Sometimes you can search for each concept separately and then combine the results of your searches afterwards.

### Combine using AND, OR, NOT

In other databases you can enter several different search terms and specify how you wish to combine them at the outset.

This is often called 'Boolean logic', after the mathematician George Boole, whose idea it was. It's simpler than it sounds:

- Combining searches using AND means that you are asking for articles each of which will feature all of your chosen search terms – '*food hygiene*' AND '*infection control*'.
- Combining using OR means that you are looking for articles which feature either (but not necessarily both) your chosen terms – '*teenage*' OR '*adolescent*'
- Combining using NOT is a way of limiting a search, ruling out articles on topics you are not interested in – '*infection*' NOT '*hospital acquired*'

### Check your spelling and typing

If your search finds no articles, check your spelling again! A good nursing or medical dictionary will help. Think too about British English and American English variations: *paediatric* or *pediatric*; *anaesthetic* or *anesthetic*.

Think of variant forms of words. You might look for articles on hand washing, hand-washing, or handwashing and get different results for each. It's always worth trying alternative forms of search terms.

For a list of common variants – including US usage – see Table 6.1.

## *Use truncation*

You can sometimes get round the problem of variant forms of word by 'truncating', or cutting short, the troublesome word. Truncation means replacing the word ending with a symbol. In BNI that symbol is '*' so if you typed 'hand*' you would retrieve all words beginning with 'hand', however they end, thus picking up 'hand-washing' and 'handwashing' as well. But beware, because this way you may also get terms you don't want – such as 'handling'.

## *Think about the timescale*

You should have some idea before you start your search of the timescale that you are looking for – indeed, you may have been told by your tutor to look only at recent articles. Occasionally you might want to look back at the development of a certain practice over time and need to find earlier items. There will be some indication when you choose your database as to the period of time covered, but you will only want articles for a part of that time. Look for ways of limiting by publication year. You probably need to choose a start and a finish date – let's say from five years ago to the present date.

Publication date can also be another useful way of broadening or narrowing your search. If your original search gives too many results, you can narrow it down to more recent articles. If you start by looking only for recent articles and don't get any results, extend your timescale a little.

## *Make good use of the 'descriptors' or 'subject headings'*

When database entries are being created, as well as recording the details of author, title, journal and so on, terms will be added to describe the subject matter of the article. These terms, called 'descriptors' or 'subject headings', are taken from a strictly controlled list or thesaurus, to give consistency. Many health databases use what's known as MeSH headings – medical subject headings.

Without getting too concerned about the detail, there is a simple way to take advantage of this. If your search gives you a reference to an article that you feel is spot-on with what you are looking for, you could take a look at the complete reference and see what subject headings have been given to that article. Then you could search again using those headings as your search terms for a highly focused search.

# 12.3 Record keeping

### Databases and searches

It is well worth keeping a note of which databases you have searched, for what period of time, keywords you used and any limits you applied. This only needs to be in the form of a note to yourself, e.g.

Searched BNI and CINAHL 2002-2008 Keywords: Infection control **and** sharps.

Then if you later decide that you need more, or different, references, you won't waste time repeating the same search. You could decide to use a different database, or the same databases for a different time period (e.g. 1995–2002), or to change your search terms.

You can incorporate this information into your assignment to demonstrate that your literature searching was structured and thorough.

### Useful references

You will need to keep a record of any references that you think look as though they would be useful to you. You often have the option of printing the references, several on a page. You may need these details later on when you are trying to find the article itself.

You will also need to reference the article if you eventually use it in your assignment. It is quick and easy to print – or email to yourself – the details when you have them in front of you and you can be sure you have all the correct information for referencing when you are finishing off your assignment.

# 12.4 From reference to actual article

When you've done your search, found some references to articles that look useful, and saved the details – then you are ready to follow up the reference and get to your goal: the actual article.

### *Easy links*

This section should really be entitled 'Link Resolvers', but how off-putting is that to anyone not particularly IT-inclined? But link resolvers really are your friends – and if you can persevere with just the next paragraph you will quickly see why.

If you're lucky, you might find this part of the process of getting from reference to article very simple. If so, it will be thanks to the new generation of 'link resolvers' now in use at many University libraries. Quite simply, these get you from database reference to full text, or to details of library print holdings, in a single click.

At our university, every article found on a database such as BNI will show a link: 'Find it @ DMU'. Click here and you will see straightaway a further link – either to the full text of the article or to the library catalogue for details of where print copies can be seen. If, for a particular reference, your university offers neither online nor print access, this will be made clear along with a link to the Interlibrary Loan process – see Section 12.6. Similar arrangements apply at many other universities.

A word of caution: sometimes there is an apparent link to full text which only leads you to another page inviting you either to subscribe to the journal or to pay for the individual article. This means that although the publishers have put the full text online, your institution has not paid a subscription to that journal which would entitle you to access it.

Do not be tempted to pay in this way – if you really need that particular article there are other cheaper ways of getting it. Neither your lecturers nor librarians are expecting you to run up such expenses to complete your assignment.

### *No easy links*

If your university library does not have link resolvers then you have to do much of the leg work yourself, and that's what we now explain – as briefly as we can. If this section may seem somewhat complex – that's because it is. Hopefully you are studying with the help of a library website assisted by 'link resolver' software; if so, you can omit this section altogether.

Journal articles are going to be available to you via one of three possible routes: online, print copy from your library, copy from another library.

- **Online**
  Online articles can often be accessed direct from the database you are searching. There will be a link next to the reference which will take you

either directly to the article or to the website of the journal, from where you can search again for the article.

■ **Print**

If there is no direct link from the database you are using, it doesn't necessarily mean that the full text is not online. On your library's website there will almost certainly be a searchable list of online journals to which students have access.

You can search this list for the *journal* title (not the title of the article). If your institution subscribes, then you can follow links on the website to find the volume, the issue and the specific article. You will of course need your reference in front of you to do this.

Occasionally, whilst most of a journal is available online, the most recent issues – typically a year – are not. These issues have been 'embargoed' so that libraries and individuals will still continue to subscribe to print versions. Older volumes, that pre-date the Internet publishing revolution, are also less likely to be available.

■ **From another library**

We look at this possibility in Section 12.6.

## 12.5 Accessing articles in print

You will need to visit the library, armed with your reference, to track down the article. Journals will be arranged first alphabetically by journal title and then in order of year and volume.

Remember that you will not normally be allowed to take printed journals out of the library, but you will be able to make photocopies of the articles you want – provided you stay within copyright law. For more details see Section 10.6.

## 12.6 Accessing articles through interlibrary loans

If your library does not have access to the article either online or in print, do not give up at this point. If you contact library staff they will probably be able to obtain the article from another library.

You will need to complete a form, which you may find on your library website, giving the full details of the reference and also the source of the reference, e.g. 'British Nursing Index', so that librarians may check the reference if there is any confusion. You'll also need to give some contact details and you may be asked to obtain a tutor's signature, just to confirm that the article is really needed and you aren't just being over-eager!

Some libraries have restrictions on the number of interlibrary requests a student can make. This is usually because it is considered that local resources are adequate to meet undergraduate assignment needs. You may also find that you will be charged for articles obtained from other libraries, but this will be a very small amount (a few pence per sheet), and little more than you would have paid to copy yourself. Bear in mind that obtaining articles from other libraries can take some time – up to two weeks to allow for time in the post and any backlogs of photocopying that libraries have to deal with.

When you are first given an assignment, it sometimes seems that the hand-in date is a long time ahead and that you don't need to think about it just yet. But it is important to do your literature search as soon as possible to allow for any trips to the library you need to make and also for time for articles to be requested and sent from other libraries. It is very frustrating to have searched a database and found articles that seem just perfect, only to find you can't use them because they wouldn't arrive in time.

## 12.7 Referencing journal articles

Once you have finished researching your assignment, you will be ready to start writing and making appropriate references to the articles you have consulted.

As we discussed in Chapter 5, it is important to cite articles, and list your references, in the correct way. Do this well and you will get credit for the thoroughness of your literature search and the quality of your research skills; you will also avoid any unintentional chance of plagiarism.

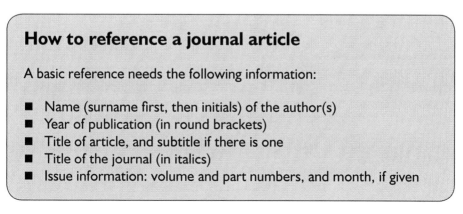

**How to reference a journal article**

A basic reference needs the following information:

- Name (surname first, then initials) of the author(s)
- Year of publication (in round brackets)
- Title of article, and subtitle if there is one
- Title of the journal (in italics)
- Issue information: volume and part numbers, and month, if given

As with book references, there are conventions about punctuation – use the examples below as a guide.

*Example*:
Potter, C. (2008) The delivery of dignity when caring for older people. *British Journal of Community Nursing*, **13**(9), 5 September, pp. 423–8.

The numbers in this example indicate volume 13 (frequently printed in bold type), issue or part number 9, and pages 423 to 428. Note that it is the title of the journal that is in italics, not the title of the article.

Many journals, including familiar ones like *Nursing Times*, *Nursing Standard* or *British Journal of Nursing*, are available either in print or online, so this form of reference would be correct whether you found the article in the printed version or online.

It would, however, be good practice to indicate that you obtained the article online, and you can do this by adding [Online] and the date you accessed it, so that your reference would read:

Potter, C. (2008) The delivery of dignity when caring for older people. *British Journal of Community Nursing*, **13**(9), 5 September, pp. 423–8. [Online] (Accessed: 23 September 2008).

It may not be appropriate (or possible) to include page numbers for some online articles.

Many journals are now only available online, so in such cases you would definitely need to include in your reference the fact that it was online and the date that you accessed it.

## 12.8 Do get help

As we have said many times in this book – don't be afraid of seeking out help from library staff at any stage. They will be pleased to help, and will know that this area of journal articles is a challenging one for many students.

# PART IV

# Internet resources

# CHAPTER 13

# The Internet: how to find high-quality websites

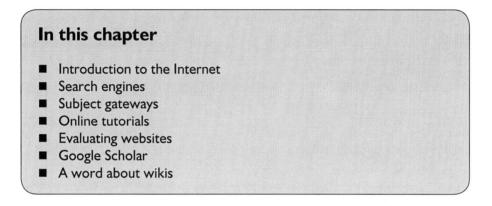

**In this chapter**

- Introduction to the Internet
- Search engines
- Subject gateways
- Online tutorials
- Evaluating websites
- Google Scholar
- A word about wikis

## 13.1 Introduction to the Internet

More than likely, the Internet will already be part of your daily life. You probably use it for all sorts of social networking and entertainment purposes – Facebook, Bebo, YouTube, iTunes etc. – and for looking up the information we all need on a regular basis – maybe cheap flights and holidays, car insurance or cinema times. And, of course, although surfing the Internet can be great fun, it's incredibly time-consuming. Now you are a student you don't have that kind of time to waste!

What we look at now is how to use the Internet effectively to find top-quality sites that you can trust to provide the information you need for your assignments.

The Internet has grown haphazardly over the years, with millions of extra pages being added every day. No structure or order has ever been imposed on it, with the result that the Internet is comparable to the biggest library in the world with all the pages from its books and journals tossed into a gigantic heap on the floor.

Where to start? Of course, if you know just what you are looking for, you can simply type the web address into your browser. Typing www.rcn.org.uk, for instance, will take you straight to the Royal College of Nursing website. But often you will not know which website to use, let alone its web address.

# 13.2 Search engines

If you are looking for information, rather than a known website, you will need to use a *search engine*. Without search engines the Internet would be unusable.

### What is a search engine?

A search engine is software which searches the Internet looking for web pages which match the terms you have typed into the search box. It then returns a list of documents in no immediately apparent order.

One component of a search engine is 'spider software' that seeks out keywords and adds them to the databases of information that the particular search engine holds. In effect, it is this automatic spider that carries out the search for you – it has not been done by a human being. People who create websites and want people to visit need to ensure that their site is submitted to one or more search engines.

There are several different search engines, some better known than others, each with its own characteristics. Not all search engines even attempt to search the whole Internet – some are specific to a particular country or language and some look at particular subjects. Of the general search engines, the best known include Google (http://www.google.co.uk/), AltaVista (http://www.altavista.com/), Yahoo! (http://www.yahoo.com/) and Ask (http://www.Ask.com/). You might like to try some of these and decide which you like best.

### Google

Google is favoured by academic institutions both because it is less gimmicky than some of the others and because it lists the websites it finds by order of the number of other sites that link to them – so the most popular appear first. It may be that for your own social purposes you prefer another search engine, but you could still use Google for finding information for academic purposes.

- Make sure you are using the UK version: http://www.google.co.uk/.
- After you have done your search you are also given the option below:

  Search:  ○ the web  ⦿ pages from the UK

  Start by choosing 'pages from the UK' to give the most relevant information for British practice. You can always expand your search to cover the whole web if you don't find what you are looking for.
- Search engines are really most useful for finding very specific pieces of information, when you have a good idea what you are looking for. For example, typing *'National Stroke Strategy'* into the Google search box will find the right pages straight away, whereas typing *'Stroke'* in the search box returns over 63,300,000 results, with the National Stroke Strategy not appearing for several pages.
- Google's Advanced Search allows you to search for a whole phrase or individual words; you can include or exclude terms or use synonyms.
- Make sure your spelling is as accurate as possible. If you are just a letter out, Google may ask you: 'Did you mean...?', but Google can't read your mind.

# 13.3  Subject gateways

The problem with the Internet is that anyone can put anything on it, with no kind of censorship or quality control, so you may be finding sites that contain information that is inappropriate, incorrect or even harmful. These are not sites you want to be using for your assignments.

Search engines just do as you ask and find sites relating to your search terms regardless of the quality of their content. To find sites of guaranteed good quality you need to use a subject gateway. Sometimes called 'portals', subject gateways are Internet directories of online resources for particular subject areas.

### Intute

In the UK we are lucky to have an excellent academic gateway called Intute (Figure 13.1). This is a free online service which sets out to provide access to the very best web resources for education and research. The service is man-

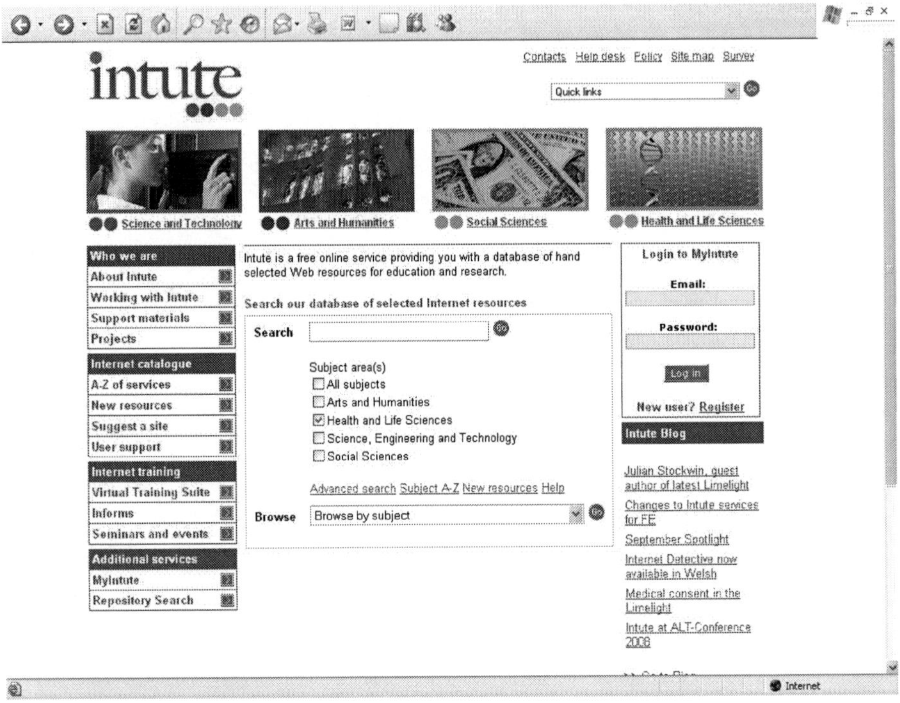

**Figure 13.1** The Intute subject gateway.

aged by a network of UK universities and partners who employ subject specialists to select and evaluate relevant websites.

The Intute gateway is divided into four academic areas:

- Arts and Humanities
- Science, Engineering and Technology
- Social Sciences
- Health and Life Sciences

The Health and Life Sciences section is led by academics from the University of Nottingham, with input from other partners. You can safely use any site found via Intute Health and Life Sciences and know that it is a reliable academic source, having been peer-reviewed and checked for quality.

### How to use Intute

Within the *Health and Life Sciences* section of Intute you can search for websites on any subject related to nursing, midwifery and allied health.

You can either 'Search' or 'Browse' this section.

**To search**, you can just type in some search terms, and you have the option to limit the search to Nursing, Midwifery and Allied Health only. Such a search for 'infection control' will find just over 150 hits. You can also choose to look just at certain types of website – for example, government publications only.

**To browse**, you can look at sites grouped under pre-selected headings. There are two lists to choose from – either 'MeSH', or Medical Subject Headings, or RCN headings. 'RCN headings' is a list created by the Royal College of Nursing using terms that will be familiar to UK health workers. The terms are listed alphabetically or you click on the letters along the top.

For students who are less than confident about their search skills, this really is an excellent service. Intute has done all the hard work for you, and sites found here can be safely used and referenced in any assignment.

## 13.4 Online tutorials

Intute also has some excellent online tutorials specially designed for health professionals in its 'Virtual Training Suite' which will show you how to use the Internet to support your studies. You can test yourself as you go and also read about how other people have used the Internet for their studies or everyday work. Half an hour very well spent!

## 13.5 Evaluating websites

Because Intute depends on input from academics and professional people, and because its standards are so high, you will not find very large numbers of sites via Intute and sometimes you might not find any. You can, of course, search for websites yourself, perhaps using Google, or by following a link from another site.

How can you know that this is a site of good enough quality for you to use? This can be a minefield: sometimes you just have to trust your own judgement, but there are clues to help you.

The Intute Virtual Training Suite has a superb tutorial for Nursing, Midwifery and Health Care called 'Judge: which websites are worth using'. You can work through it at your own pace as many times as you like. The following sections (p. 97) on the 'three Ws' and what you can learn from the website URL are a shortened version of the Judge tutorial which we publish here with kind permission of Intute.

### A student nurse on the Internet

Cheryl is a student in the second year of her Diploma in Nursing Studies and is currently on a placement for care of the elderly.

She has been asked to do a case study on one of her patients. She chooses a lady who has developed a sacral pressure sore during recovery from a hip replacement operation.

Wishing to write some introductory background to the case, and certain that the Internet must have plenty of information on the subject, Cheryl types **pressure sores** into the search box of **Google**.

She's used Google many times before, and found it easy to use and productive. Unfortunately, on this occasion, her enquiry produces more than five million hits, and though some of them on the first page look promising, she is not confident about her ability to choose the best sites.

She remembers **Intute:Nursing** which she's been told about in one of her lectures. She knows that it only contains resources that have been objectively evaluated.

Cheryl types **pressure sores** in the Intute search box and finds that the number of hits is just over 20, and that for each item an informative abstract is given.

Among the resources cited are a UK **Department of Health policy update on wound care and tissue viability** and a **quick reference guide to assessing and grading pressure ulcers** published by the Nursing Standard.

**Armed with these and other authoritative sources listed on the *Intute: Nursing* site Cheryl is soon able to put together a background section for her case study essay.**

**A success story, reproduced with the kind permission of Intute.**

**Figure 13.2** Intute tutorial for student nurses on using the Internet. *Text and illustrations reproduced by kind permission of Intute.*

Ask yourself the 'three Ws' of the World Wide Web: Who? Where? When?

- **Who?** Anyone can put information of any kind on the Internet – it doesn't have to be truthful, helpful, or trustworthy. You need to ask yourself who has written the information and what their motive was for doing so. On the site you should be able to find the name of the author; the name of an organisation publishing the information; an 'About us' section; some contact details.
- **Where?** Which country does this information come from? This may be especially important for health students as you will be expected to be looking at British practice in your assignments. There should be some indication of country of origin on the website, even if only as part of the URL (web address).
- **When?** Look for some indication of when the pages were created or when last updated – often to be found at the very bottom. Sometimes quite good sites are created in a burst of enthusiasm and then are not kept up to date, perhaps because it takes a lot of time. An 'About us' page may say how regularly the site is updated.

Keep in mind that you are looking for information from a trustworthy individual or organisation, originating in your own country if possible, and which is still current.

### URL: Uniform Resource Locator

The URL – Uniform (or Universal) Resource Locator – of a website is what we would probably call a web address. It has a familiar form of several little sections linked by dots – e.g. www.library.dmu.ac.uk.

You can get lots of clues about the origin of the information if you know how to interpret the URL. For instance, it's not hard to see that this website will contain information provided by the library of De Montfort University. Table 13.1 shows an easy way of decoding URLs you may come across.

## 13.6 Google Scholar

Google Scholar is an attempt to search not the whole Internet, but only sites of academic importance. It includes some material not normally available via a standard Google search, from the 'deep' or 'hidden' web, e.g. from library catalogues or online journals.

**Table 13.1**

| Code | Meaning | Example |
|------|---------|---------|
| .ac | From an academic or educational organisation | www.library.dmu.ac.uk library of De Montfort University |
| .co or .com | From a commercial organisation | www.amazon.co.uk Amazon online bookshop |
| .gov | From a government or local government organisation | www.dh.gov.uk Department of Health |
| .nhs | UK National Health Service | www.library.nhs.uk National Library for Health |
| .org | From a non-governmental, non-profit making organisation | www.bhf.org.uk British Heart Foundation |

The last part of the URL is often a country code, e.g. .uk for United Kingdom; .au for Australia and so on.

If you use the Basic Search facility you may find that you are getting thousands of results, many of which are not at all relevant to your area of study.

Instead, you can use Advanced Search (Figure 13.3) which will give you the option of choosing a subject area to search in. Select 'Medicine, Pharmacology and Veterinary Science'. There is nothing specifically for nursing or related health disciplines. Advanced Search also offers a range of useful features.

### Limit your search to recent articles

You can do this at the start of your search by asking Scholar to 'return articles published between' two dates (leave the second date blank if you want the most recent information). Alternatively, wait until you get your search results, and click on 'Recent articles': your results will be sorted with the most recent first.

### Set preferences

If you go to Scholar Preferences you will find a range of choices. The most important of these is 'Library links'. If you are working away from your academic institution, type in the name of your institution: e.g. De Montfort University. You can choose up to three, as long as you are eligible.

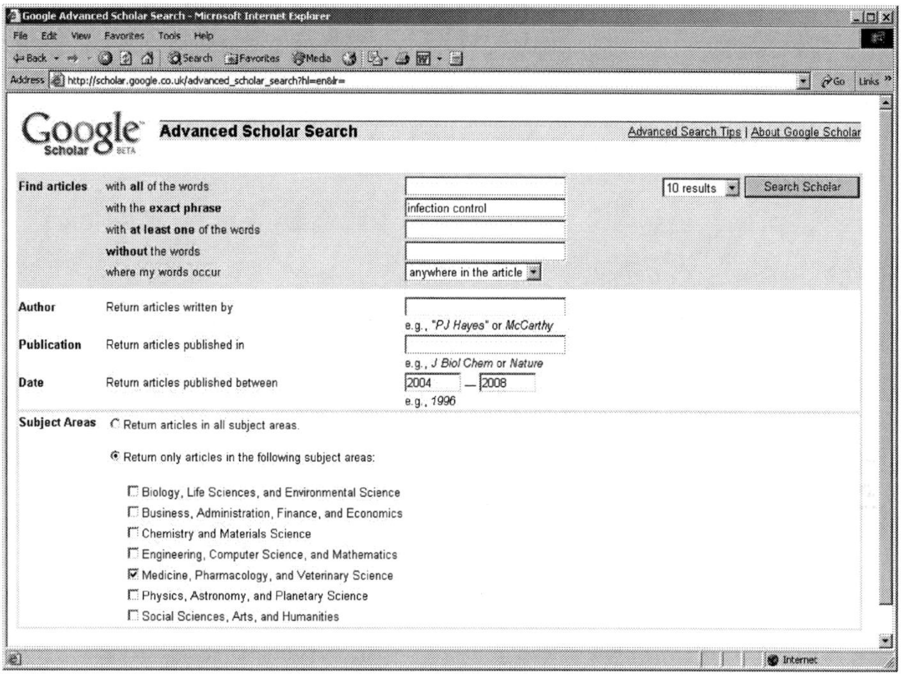

**Figure 13.3** Google Scholar's Advanced Search.

When you save your preferences, Google Scholar will remember them for your subsequent searches and offer links to the full text of articles from journals that your library has online subscriptions to. Google Scholar does not give you wider access than that offered by your library, though you may be able to see some additional abstracts.

If you are working on a computer on campus, you won't need to set preferences, as Google Scholar will recognise you as a member of that institution.

You can also opt for pages in English only.

### Author searches

In Advanced Search you can search for articles on a particular topic by a specific author.

Alternatively, if you do a keyword search only, on the left of your search results you will see a list of authors' names (Figure 13.4). These are people who have published significant amounts of material in the subject and you could click on one of their names to view their work.

Google Scholar is popular because it looks familiar, is quick and easy to use and for many purposes will give you a good enough result.

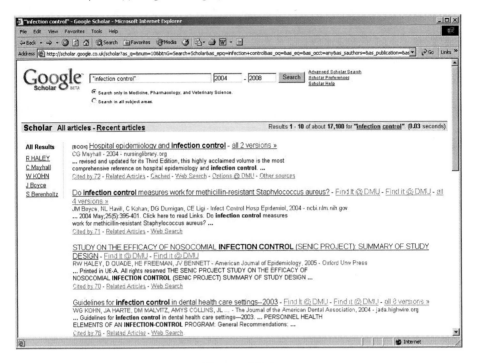

**Figure 13.4**

However, one of the problems with Google Scholar is that Google is reluctant to state exactly what material is included, from which publishers, and what is excluded. In particular, there is no clear statement of the time span covered and many recent articles are excluded. Google Scholar is particularly strong in the area of medicine and yet it is believed that it is up to a year behind PubMed in the articles it has indexed. It lacks many of the advanced searching features of specialist subject databases so it is difficult to narrow your search down to find a few highly relevant articles. At the present time, Google Scholar can't compete with British Nursing Index, CINAHL or some of the other health databases in meeting the needs of nursing and related health students. With the might of Google behind it, Scholar will develop and improve and is a resource to watch for the future.

## 13.7 A word about wikis

A 'wiki' is a website that is created collaboratively. It is designed to be very easy to add to or alter. The term derives from 'wiki wiki', which means 'quickly' in Hawaiian.

Wikipedia is an online encyclopaedia written collaboratively by its users. One person will write an article and post it on the site for others to read. The next person who reads it may feel he knows more about the subject and add some information – or he may disagree with the first writer and make some 'corrections', which may be more or less accurate than the original content.

All of which is great fun and has produced a constantly evolving encyclopaedia which can give you good enough answers to the sorts of questions that often crop up. But Wikipedia is not an academic source. In fact, it is the exact opposite, as we do not know who writes the articles, where the information comes from, why it is being written or when.

It is not peer-reviewed or quality controlled in any meaningful sense. You should not rely on information from Wikipedia, nor should you cite it in academic assignments.

In Chapters 14 to 16 we look at how to use the Internet to find some specific types of information.

## How to reference an Internet site

First you need to think carefully about what it is that you are using. If it is a book, report, journal article or similar you need to be following the referencing rules for the type of material.

A basic reference for a website you have used would need to include:

- author – very often a body of people
- name or title of the site (in italics)
- date that the information was published or last updated
- type of resource – eg e-mail or www
- Responsible organisation – this may be the same as the author
- URL or web address where site can be found
- date you accessed it – especially important as material can change or disappear from the site altogether

If you can't find a date, you can use (n.d.), which stands for 'no date', instead.

*Example:*
Royal College of Nursing (2008) *Think positive: let's end the stigma of HIV.* WWW. Royal College of Nursing. Available from: http://www.rcn.org. uk/newsevents/campaigns/think_positive/hiv_facts [Accessed 23/09/08]

*or*

BBC (2008) *BBC headroom: do you ever feel like you're losing it?* WWW. BBC. Available from: http://www.bbc.co.uk/headroom/newsand-events/programmes/losing it.shtml [Accessed 23/09/08]

# CHAPTER 14

# Statistics and images

---

## In this chapter

- Using statistics
- Local and regional statistics
- National and international statistics
- Statistics from interest groups
- Images

---

## 14.1 Introduction to statistics

Appropriate use of statistics can be an excellent way of enlivening your essay and putting your work into context.

Consider the difference between these two possible opening paragraphs to your essay:

---

### Essay version 1

Lung cancer is one of the commonest cancers in the UK and affects many people. It is more common in men than in women.

### Essay version 2

Lung cancer is one of the commonest cancers in the UK. 'Until the late 1990s lung cancer was the most frequently occurring cancer in the UK; it has now been overtaken by breast cancer but still accounts for around 1 in

---

7 new cancer cases, that is, 38,598 new patients diagnosed in 2005'. The chart shows new cases by gender and nation (Cancer Research UK, 2008).

Number of new cases and rates of lung cancer, UK, 2005.

|  | England | Wales | Scotland | N. Ireland | UK |
|---|---|---|---|---|---|
| **Cases** | | | | | |
| Males | 18,037 | 1,226 | 2,480 | 516 | 22,259 |
| Females | 13,000 | 920 | 2,063 | 356 | 16,339 |
| Persons | 31,037 | 2,146 | 4,543 | 872 | 38,598 |

In the second version, some facts and figures from a reputable website add authority to the opening statement. The second opening would be much more impressive, yet those statistics took only a minute or two to find from Cancer Research UK's website.

The Internet has made vast amounts of statistical information readily available to us. Much statistical data that was once published annually in print is now only available on the Internet, where it can be updated much more readily.

As ever with the Internet, the problem lies in deciding what is trustworthy information and what is rather more dubious. Intute's Health and Life Sciences gateway, discussed in Chapter 13, is a good source of reliable statistical websites. Select Nursing, Midwifery and Allied Health and put Statistics in the search box.

If you are finding statistics sites yourself, remember to evaluate them carefully, as discussed in Chapter 13.

### Searching for stats – a couple of tips

■ You can find statistics relating to many common conditions with a Google search. Key in the condition you are looking for and the word 'statistics'. Be sure that you are finding UK sites and remember to evaluate carefully.
■ You can also use databases to find statistical information. For example, a search on British Nursing Index for 'Suicide' and 'Statistics' found 15 references to journal articles consisting largely of statistics, many coming from specialist statistical journals such as *Health Statistics Quarterly*.

You will find that there are any number of websites offering statistics, and it can be difficult to know where to start. The next sections provide an overview of some key sites which together offer a wide range of reliable statistics.

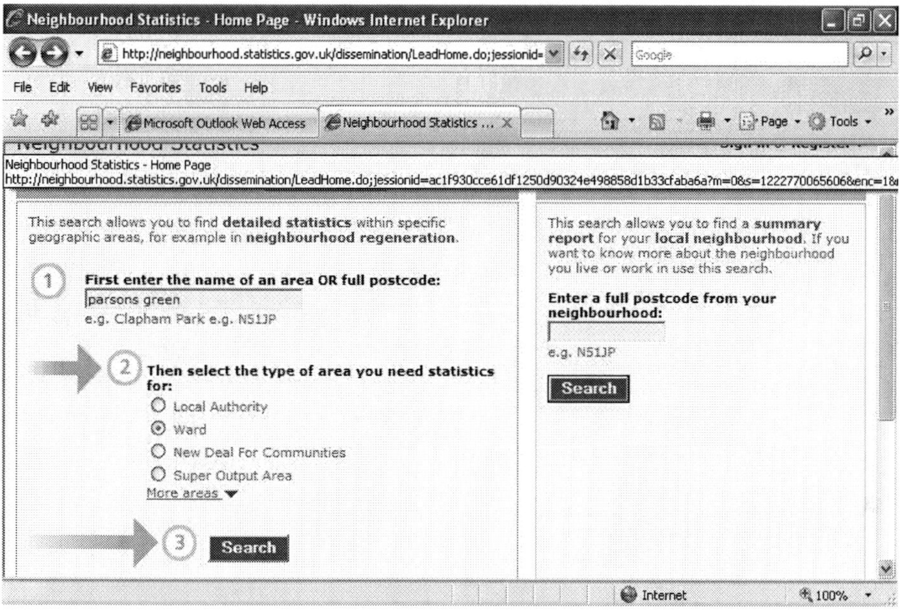

**Figure 14.1** Neighbourhood Statistics.

## 14.2 Local statistics

The richest source of statistical data at a local level is the UK government site called Neighbourhood Statistics, which you can find at http://neighbourhood. statistics.gov.uk/.

You can search Neighbourhood Statistics by postcode or by area name and find a wealth of data about the area in which you live or work.

You will then have access to very detailed statistics relating to the area. You will see from the list below that some are more obviously relevant to health care students than others. Statistics cover:

- 2001 census data for the neighbourhood
- Access to services
- Community wellbeing/social environment
- Crime and safety
- Economic deprivation
- Education, skills and training
- Health and care
- Housing
- Indicators – summary statistics of themes across all topics
- Indices of deprivation and classification

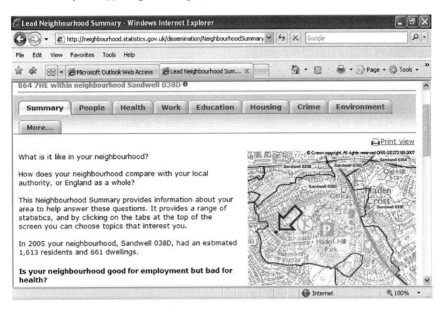

**Figure 14.2** Neighbourhood summary – 1.

- People and society: population and migration
- Physical environment
- Work deprivation

Within these categories you can find many 'sub-sets' of specific data. You can build up a picture of how affluent an area is, how much unemployment or homelessness, what the levels of education are like, and so on – all the factors which impact on the health of the population.

If this looks like more information than you can cope with – don't panic! There is an alternative search entitled 'Neighbourhood Summary' which will produce an overview of the area with simpler statistical information: see Figure 14.2.

If you click on any of the tabs – People, Health, Work, Education and so on – they will lead you to further statistics.

Figure 14.3 is a simple visual representation of levels of deprivation in one postcode area. Have a look at the data for your own area – does it correspond with your own sense of what life is like there?

Other sources of local statistics are Strategic Health Authorities or NHS Trusts. These produce annual reports, often focusing on a particular area of activity each year. Print copies of these reports may be held in libraries, while online versions are available from the Health Authority or Trust websites. You can find lists of Strategic Health Authorities and Trusts in the Service Directory area of NHS Choices (http://www.nhs.uk/servicedirectories/) with links through to the individual websites.

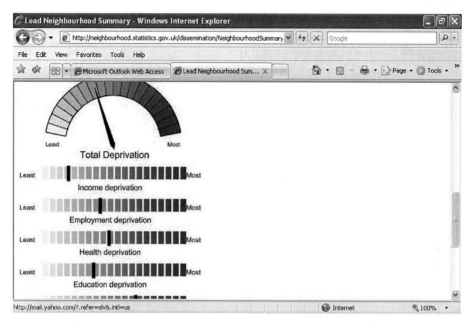

**Figure 14.3** Neighbourhood summary – 2.

## 14.3 Regional statistics

In England, there are nine regional 'public health observatories' whose role is to gather information to provide local agencies with public health data and information to inform health policy. Statistics can be found on their websites (Table 14.2).

**Table 14.2** Public health observatories.

| | |
|---|---|
| East Midlands | http://www.empho.org.uk/ |
| Eastern Region | http://www.erpho.org.uk/ |
| London | http://www.lpho.org.uk/ |
| North East | http://www.nepho.org.uk/ |
| North West | http://www.nwpho.org.uk/ |
| South East | http://www.sepho.org.uk/ |
| South West | http://www.swpho.org.uk/ |
| West Midlands | http://www.wmpho.org.uk/ |
| Yorkshire and Humber | http://www.yhpho.org.uk/ |

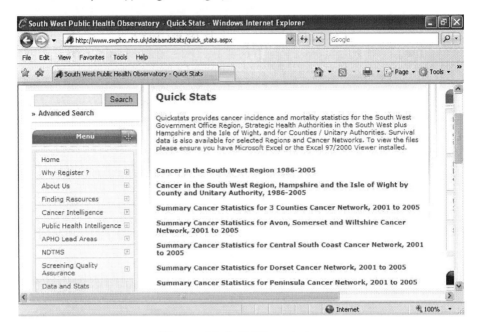

**Figure 14.4** PHO statistics.

Figure 14.4 is an example of the kinds of statistics available from one PHO.

There is also a website for the overall body, Association of Public Health Observatories, and this has a Health Profile for every local authority in England which uses key indicators to capture a picture of the nation's health at local level – especially health inequalities between areas – including information on child health inequalities.

Association of Public Health Observatories: http://www.apho.org.uk/

There are separate Public Health Observatories for Scotland, Wales, and Ireland and Northern Ireland with comparable information and they can be found at the following web addresses:

Ireland and Northern Ireland:    http://www.inispho.org.uk/
Scotland:    http://www.scotpho.org.uk/
Wales (Wales Centre for Health)    http://www.wch.wales.org.uk/

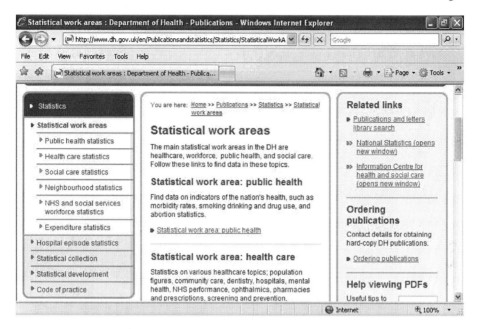

**Figure 14.5** Department of Health website.

## 14.4 National statistics

The Department of Health website at http://www.dh.gov.uk/ (Figure 14.5) is a rich source of statistical data on health and health care. They are concentrated in four main areas: health care, workforce, public health and social care.

Figure 14.6 is an example from the healthcare area, of some statistical data relating to emergency admission statistics for children and young people 1996–2006.

There are also links to other statistical websites, most notably HES or Hospital Episode Statistics (which can also be found at http://www.hesonline.nhs. uk/). HES records patient details such as age, sex, date of admission and length of stay, diagnosis and treatment.

## 14.5 International statistics

Statistics from around the world may be of less interest to you than UK ones, but can also be useful to set a context for your work. You might want to ask 'Why

DH_083711[1].pdf - Adobe Reader

File  Edit  View  Document  Tools  Window  Help

[ 10 / 25 ]  [ 80.6% ]  Find

Trends in Children's Care - Emergency Admission Statistics, 1996-2006

**Table 1**
**Emergency admissions for patients aged 0-19 years and 20 and over, percentage year-on-year changes and admission rates per 1,000 population in age group**

| | 0-19 years | | | | 20+ years | | | |
|---|---|---|---|---|---|---|---|---|
| | Admi'ns | % change in admi'ns | Admi'ns per 1,000 pop'n | % change in admi'ns per 1,000 pop'n | Admi'ns | % change in admi'ns | Admi'ns per 1,000 pop'n | % change in admi'ns per 1,000 pop'n |
| 1996/97 | 708,142 | | 57.8 | | 2,812,694 | | 77.6 | |
| 1997/98 | 739,480 | 4.4% | 60.0 | 3.7% | 2,885,323 | 2.6% | 79.4 | 2.4% |
| 1998/99 | 741,044 | 0.2% | 59.8 | - 0.3% | 2,995,239 | 3.8% | 82.2 | 3.5% |
| 1999/00 | 730,189 | -1.5% | 58.8 | - 1.6% | 3,039,609 | 1.5% | 83.0 | 0.9% |
| 2000/01 | 731,520 | 0.2% | 59.2 | 0.6% | 3,086,854 | 1.6% | 83.7 | 0.9% |
| 2001/02 | 740,356 | 1.2% | 60.1 | 1.5% | 3,070,487 | - 0.5% | 82.7 | - 1.2% |
| 2002/03 | 726,082 | -1.9% | 58.9 | - 2.0% | 3,138,889 | 2.2% | 84.1 | 1.7% |
| 2003/04 | 757,479 | 4.3% | 61.3 | 4.1% | 3,368,805 | 7.3% | 89.8 | 6.8% |
| 2004/05 | 783,889 | 3.5% | 63.4 | 3.4% | 3,578,781 | 6.2% | 94.8 | 5.6% |
| 2005/06 | 833,555 | 6.3% | 67.5 | 6.4% | 3,760,708 | 5.1% | 98.7 | 4.2% |
| 2006/07 | 833,771 | 0.03% | 67.6 | 0.1% | 3,805,770 | 1.2% | 99.1 | 0.3% |

**Figure 14.6** Sample statistics from the Department of Health website.

does the UK have one of the highest rates of teenage pregnancy in Europe?' or 'How do rates of heart disease compare between the UK and the USA?'.

Table 14.3 shows some useful websites and the sort of information they contain.

## 14.6  Statistics from interest groups

The websites of interest groups representing people who have particular illnesses or conditions can be very good sources of facts and figures relating to those conditions. Two good examples are provided by the Mental Health Foundation and Cancer Research UK.

■ **Mental Health Foundation**: http://www.mentalhealth.org.uk/. This site offers clear and simple statistics relating to such questions as 'How many people experience mental health problems?', 'How common is suicide?' or 'How common is self-harm?'.

## Table 14.3

| World Health Organization | http://www.who.int/en/ | The coordinating body for health between United Nations members. Data and Statistics include:<br>(1) WHOSIS (Statistical Information System): mortality, morbidity, risk factors, services and healthcare systems<br>(2) Global Infobase Online: chronic diseases and risk factors<br>(3) Global Health Atlas: infectious diseases<br>(4) Regional statistics |
|---|---|---|
| European Health for All | http://www.euro.who.int/ | A European slant on WHO statistical date. Includes: (1) Data – European statistical databases and links to other useful websites; and (2) Evidence – country profiles, world health report, European health report, atlas of health |
| UNICEF | http://www.childinfo.org/ | Monitors the situation of children and women throughout the world. Website has extensive data on child survival, nutrition, maternal health, newborn care, child protection and more, by country |

■ **Cancer Research UK**: http://info.cancerresearchuk.org/; Figure 14.7. The extensive CancerStats section, designed for health professionals, provides statistics on every type of cancer.

# 14.7 Images

In the same way that statistics can enrich and enliven your written work, so too can a carefully chosen image. Indeed, your image might be a representation of some statistical data – a bar chart or graph, for example.

In particular, a poster or PowerPoint presentation could be greatly enhanced by a suitable picture. You may well find an image in a book or journal article that you wish to use. The Internet is also a rich source of images. In either case, you need to be aware of copyright restrictions (see Chapter 5). Look closely at websites for copyright guidance and be sure to reference any image you use.

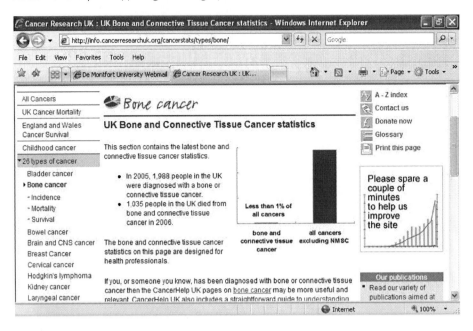

**Figure 14.7** Statistics published on the Cancer Research UK website.

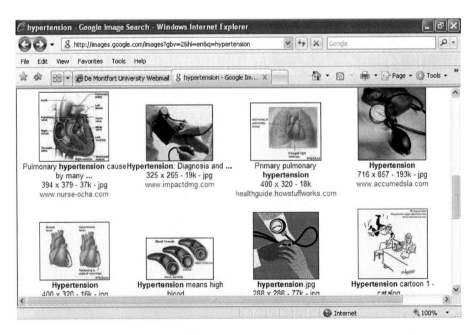

**Figure 14.8** A Google images search.

## Googling for images

If you use Google at http://www.google.co.uk/ and select 'Images', you can search for an image in much the same way that you might search for a text-based site. Google will find you images from all over the web, with no guarantee of quality – you will need to judge images carefully, asking yourself how reliable is the site the image came from, as we discussed in Chapter 13.

A search of Google Images for 'Hypertension' revealed over 800,000 images from a wide range of sources. Figure 14.8 shows a selection, ranging from detailed diagrams to cartoons.

In each case you can click on the image to view it in context on the website it is taken from, which should help you to judge its quality.

You can also find images via Intute: Health and Life Sciences (http://www. intute.ac.uk/healthandlifesciences/). You would need to use the Advanced Search, select Nursing, Midwifery and Allied Health, key in a search term, e.g. Surgery, and then 'Filter by resource type': Images. This will find you a

**Figure 14.9** A picture is worth a thousand words!

Title: Youngsters Receive Childhood Immunization
Date: 03/09/2007
Description : GLASGOW, UNITED KINGDOM – SEPTEMBER 03: A young boy reacts to receiving a immunization jab at a health centre in Glasgow September 3, 2007 in Glasgow, Scotland. Medical experts still believe the MMR jab is safe and that the vaccine does not cause autism. (Photo by Jeff J Mitchell/Getty Images)
Photographer: Jeff J Mitchell

limited range of images that you can use with confidence knowing they are from reputable sites.

In all these cases, there may well be copyright restrictions on the use of images. There is an excellent database of copyright-free images, called Education Image Gallery (Figure 14.9), at http://www.edina.ac.uk/eig/. You would need to log in with your Athens account details if your institution subscribes to this database. The majority of the pictures are very general and would not add much to the academic content of your work, but a well-chosen picture can make considerable impact.

One further source of images is the National Library for Health (http://www.library.nhs.uk/). Log in with an NHS Athens account (see Section 2.4), type in a search term and select Images. Alternatively, go to the Images section to see a full list of available image sets to choose from. We look again at the National Library for Health in Chapter 17.

---

## How to reference an image

If you have used an image that you found in a book or journal article, the image may not necessarily be the work of the author of the book, in which case you need to reference both the image and the book.

*Example:*
Maslow, A. *Maslow's hierarchy of needs.* [Diagram] In: Gross, R (2005) *Psychology: the science of mind and behaviour*, 5th ed. London: Hodder Arnold.

If you have used an online image, your reference should include:

- description or title of image (in italics)
- year image was created
- statement that it is an online image
- originator of image – if this information is available
- URL where image can be found
- date accessed

*Example:*
This is an example of a reference for an image taken from the Education Image Gallery, where the name of the photographer was given:

*Visiting day* (2001) [Online image] McVay, R. Available from: http://eig.edina.ac.uk [Accessed 23/10/08]

# CHAPTER 15

# Patient information and health in the news

In this chapter we are looking at some less academic types of information which can nevertheless be very important to your studies.

There is a huge amount of information written especially for the general public which can be extremely helpful, but which has to be treated with some caution.

## 15.1 Patient information

Reading information intended for patients can be helpful to you if you have only very limited knowledge of a condition, or if you want to know what kinds of ideas patients might have, or if your task is to write a leaflet or create a poster that would be an aid to patient education.

You can use and reference patient information in your assignments, but you do need to understand that it is written with a reader in mind who has little or no knowledge of the subject. It isn't a substitute for the academic books, journals and websites you should also be using.

### Finding patient information

There is a great deal of information published for patients in a variety of forms – the difficulty is not in finding it but in judging the quality of it.

You will probably see leaflets on display in a chemist's shop, health centre or doctor's surgery. These are often produced by organisations such as the British Medical Association or British Heart Foundation. The problem with these leaflets is that you can never be sure that they are up to date. Instead of collecting leaflets you are advised to go to appropriate websites, where you can be more confident that the information is current. You can often print off leaflets or factsheets from the website.

### Patient information websites

Here are some recommended websites for information with patients and the general public in mind.

- **NHS Choices**: http://www.nhs.uk/ is the official website of the NHS and designed for use by the general public. Its main sections are:
  - *Living Well*: general advice for healthy living
  - *Health A–Z*: search facility for information on conditions and treatment
  - *Find Services*: information on local health facilities
- **BBC Health**: http://www.bbc.co.uk/health/ has a searchable list of illness and conditions, very clearly explained.
- **Patient UK**: http://www.patient.co.uk/ is good for the following types of information, written by GPs with patients in mind, and fully searchable:
  - Health and disease leaflets
  - Patient support organisations and self-help groups
  - All about medicine
  - Healthy lifestyle and preventing illness
  - Tests and investigations
  - Directory of health-related websites
  - Links to health, lifestyle and disease videos
- **British Medical Association**: http://www.bma.org.uk/ has a 'Patients and public' section with links to many other recommended websites.

### Charities or interest groups

These are a very good source of patient information. Good examples include:

- **Contact a Family**: http://www.cafamily.org.uk/
  Contact a Family is the only UK-wide charity providing advice, information and support to the parents of all disabled children. It has an online directory of patient-friendly information for children and adults with disabilities, serious health conditions and rare disorders. There is very comprehensive medical information, advice on living with serious conditions and contact details for support groups, for over 1,200 conditions.
- **Cancerbackup**: http://www.cancerbackup.org.uk/
  This site claims to answer 'Any question on any cancer'. It offers extremely comprehensive information, clearly expressed, very easy to find, from a highly reputable organisation. There is also a searchable database of answers to over 1,000 important questions on cancer.
- **Mental Health Foundation**: http://www.mentalhealth.org.uk/ has easily searchable information on all aspects of mental health (Figure 15.1).
- **SpecialistInfo.com**: http://www.specialistinfo.com/
  Primarily a database of UK consultants and GPs, this site also has a very comprehensive directory of health charity websites with links through to their websites. Although some areas of the website require you to register and log in, the Charity Directory is freely available. If there is a reputable charity website for a condition, you will find it here.

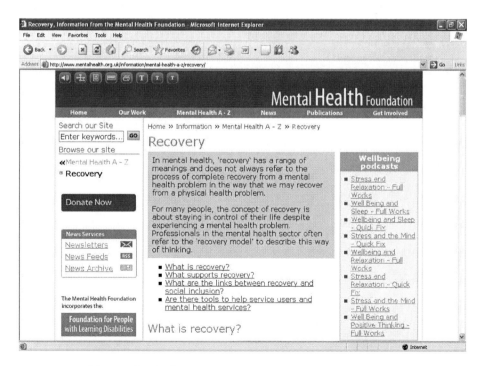

**Figure 15.1** The Mental Health Foundation website.

## 15.2 Health in the news

Health stories are constantly in the news, whether they be about a new wonder drug, another health scare or a crisis in the NHS. You may read something in a newspaper or magazine, or see something on television, that sparks your interest or relates to an area you are studying. Nothing could be more current than this week's news stories – but you do need to use them with caution. Stories are often sensationalised to sell papers and the real stories may be less dramatic.

Reliable websites for finding health news include BBC Health (http://www.bbc.co.uk/health/) and *The Guardian* (http://www.guardian.co.uk/health/).

**Patient UK** has an online 'Patient UK newspaper' of current stories gleaned from all over the press, UK and further afield. It gives you both the story and also some useful further information.

Even the best of websites often will not give you sufficient information of the right kind to include in an academic assignment. You need to be asking 'Where did this story originate?' and 'Is this really what the research found?'.

The official website of the NHS: NHS Choices, at http://www.nhs.uk/, or via the National Library for Health, has a feature called 'Behind the Headlines' (Figure 15.2), where you can find a range of recent health stories. For each

**Figure 15.2** NHS Choices.

one, the story is told, including the newspapers or television channels that covered it, and the following questions answered:

- Where did the story come from?
- What kind of scientific study was this?
- What were the results of the study?
- What interpretations did the researchers draw from these results?
- What does the NHS Knowledge Service make of this study?

Not every topic will be covered, but this is a very good indication of the sort of questions you should be asking about a health story.

The Intute: Health and Life Sciences site at http://www.intute.ac.uk/healthandlifesciences/ has a feature called 'Hot Topics'. This has much more limited coverage than 'Behind the Headlines' as it only covers one topic per month, often linked to a special day, such as International Childhood Cancer Day. Intute summarises the issues and provides links to recommended websites.

---

## How to reference a newspaper article

This is very similar to a journal article reference. The reference should include:

- Author, if one is named
- Year of publication (in round brackets)
- Title of article
- Title of newspaper (in italics)
- Day and month of publication
- Page number

If no author is named, you can start with the title, followed by the date.

*Example:*
Carvel, J. (2008) Revealed: the nine types of heavy drinker. *The Guardian*, 17 September, p. 10.

If you found your information in an online newspaper, you need to make this clear in your reference.

*Example:*
Lipsett, A. (2008) Pupils to get lessons in fighting depression: thousands will learn the positive thinking techniques used in cognitive behavioural therapy. *The Guardian*, 18 September. [Online] Available at: http://www.guardian.co.uk/. (Accessed: 23/10/08)

---

# CHAPTER 16

# Information for evidence-based health care

## In this chapter

- What is evidence-based health care?
- Cochrane Library
- CKS: Clinical Knowledge Summaries
- NICE: National Institute for Health and Clinical Excellence
- Bandolier: online journal

## 16.1 Evidence-based health care

Modern nursing, midwifery and allied health care disciplines are all regarded as 'evidence-based' professions. This means that practitioners will seek to use the best evidence that is currently available to them to guide them in making decisions about the care of individual patients. This approach depends heavily on carrying out research, making the findings of that research available to professionals, and encouraging people to integrate research findings into their practice.

You may well be told to look for evidence to support some particular nursing practice, or you may feel that it would add a lot of weight to your argument in an academic essay or dissertation if you could cite the evidence. There are several very good sources of evidence.

With most of the information we have considered so far – books, journals, websites – we have focused on ways of finding the best quality information possible, and implicit in that is that it should be based on evidence. However, there are some specific sources of evidence to support health care, and we look at these in this chapter.

# 16.2 The Cochrane Library

The Cochrane Library (http://www.cochrane.org/) is considered to be the 'top of the tree' of health care evidence. It is called a library because it is a collection of online databases. The databases we looked at in Chapter 11 were designed to answer the question: 'What academic articles can I find on the subject I'm working on?'. If this is what you want to know, so that you can choose a few good, relevant articles on which to base your assignment, then the Cochrane Library is not what you need.

The scope of the Cochrane Library is the effectiveness, including cost effectiveness, of health interventions. The Cochrane Library holds details of various kinds of research around this and should only be used for this purpose.

The Cochrane Library can be used to answer questions like:

- What is the best treatment for...?
- How effective is a certain health intervention?
- Is this treatment better than that treatment?

The most important of the Cochrane databases is the **Cochrane Database of Systematic Reviews** which contains the full text of systematic reviews published by the Cochrane Collaboration.

Each review addresses a clearly formulated question, such as: Can antibiotics help in alleviating the symptoms of a sore throat? The research has been stringently reviewed to establish whether or not there is conclusive evidence.

A systematic review will provide the best quality evidence available. If there is no systematic review for your subject, the other databases provide information on other good quality reviews. They are:

- **Database of Abstracts of Reviews of Effects**: these are reviews which have not been carried out by the Cochrane Collaboration but are nevertheless of high quality. The abstract summarises the review and also comments on its quality.
- **Cochrane Central Register of Controlled Trials**: this contains references to published articles about randomised controlled trials (RCTs). It is the most comprehensive database of RCTs, but there is no critical appraisal.
- **Cochrane Methodology Register**: this is a database of journal articles, books etc. reporting on methods used in conducting controlled trials.
- **Health Technology Assessment Database**: this brings together details of health technology assessments (studies of the medical, social and economic implications of health care interventions) from around the world.
- **NHS Economic Evaluation Database**: this has summaries of information about the costs and effects of different health care interventions, which are critically appraised.

Searching the Cochrane Library for evidence could give you various different answers to your question:

- A list of interventions that do or don't work – a **positive** answer on which to base changes in practice
- Evidence that a certain practice cannot be recommended in the light of present knowledge – a **negative** answer, but at least we know something doesn't work.
- A lack of evidence one way or another – a fairly **neutral** answer which may indicate a need for further research.

When you search the Cochrane Library you can search all its databases simultaneously, but the results will be presented by individual database so it's useful to know what inclusion in a particular database means. If you do find an item in the Cochrane Database of Systematic Reviews, be very careful about printing it out – reviews are often very long indeed and the abstract is likely to give you more than enough information.

If you search the Cochrane Library and get no results, it doesn't mean that your search has failed. Zero results is an answer in itself – that there is, as yet, no completed research of a sufficiently high standard to be included.

# 16.3 CKS – Clinical Knowledge Summaries

CKS is a source of clinical knowledge for the NHS about the common conditions managed in primary and first contact care.

Practical and reliable, it helps health care professionals make evidence-based decisions about the health care of their patients with confidence and provides the know-how to put these decisions into action safely.

Information held on CKS (http://cks.library.nhs.uk/) includes:

- Concise summaries on how to manage almost 500 clinical situations – all based on the best available evidence
- Detailed up-to-date clinical knowledge on common acute and chronic conditions, and disease prevention
- Information on the incidence of influenza and other notifiable infectious diseases
- Access to patient information leaflets developed by NHS Direct

The main part of CKS is its Topic Reviews, giving an up-to-date account of clinical knowledge on conditions and symptoms commonly seen in primary care. You can either search the A–Z index of these for very specific topics (e.g. burns and scalds; gout; migraine; febrile convulsions) or choose from a more general list of clinical specialties (e.g. men's health; child health; mental health; sexual health; pregnancy). You need to register on the site to gain access to all areas.

## 16.4 NICE – National Institute for Health and Clinical Excellence

NICE (http://www.nice.org.uk/) provides national guidance (Figure 16.1) on promoting good health and preventing and treating ill health.

NICE is a special service for England and Wales, whose role is to provide patients, health professionals and the public with authoritative guidance on current 'best practice'. NICE guidance covers three areas:

■ **Clinical guidance**: the appropriate treatment and care of patients with specific diseases and conditions within the NHS in England and Wales

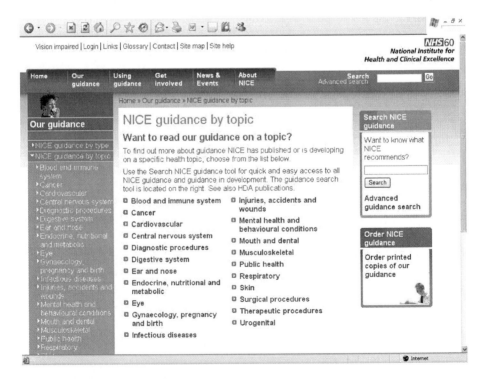

**Figure 16.1** NICE guidance.

- **Technology appraisals**: the use of new and existing medicines and treatments within the NHS in England and Wales
- **Interventional procedures**: the safety and efficiency of interventions used for diagnosis or treatment

NICE is often in the news for some negative reason – sometimes because they have failed to endorse a new drug on which people are pinning their hopes; sometimes because their considerations seem to be taking a long time. However, you can be certain that when NICE guidance is published it is based on the best possible current evidence. You will not find NICE guidance for every aspect of health, but the database of guidance is building steadily.


## 16.5 *Bandolier*: an online journal

*Bandolier* (http://www.ebandolier.com/) is a monthly journal of evidence for healthcare, published since 1994, which has been online only since 2007. The idea behind *Bandolier* is to express information about evidence of effectiveness as simply as possible, in a series of bullet points of things that work and things that don't. The information is largely derived from PubMed and the Cochrane Library and presented in the form of online journal articles by the *Bandolier* research team. Each month the focus is on evidence in a particular area, but all previous months are still available on the website.

The *Bandolier* website also has the following:

- **Knowledge Library**: an A–Z listing of evidence by topic.
- **Healthy Living**: a section described as 'for us ordinary folk' looking at evidence relating to health factors in every day life. A random sample includes Body Mass Index; Healthy use of alcohol, tea and coffee; 10 tips for healthy living; Mobile phones, magnetic fields and cancer.
- **Extended essays** on evidence-related topics.
- **Learning Zone**: information on how to approach and understand evidence.
- **EBM glossary**: simple explanations of the terms used in evidence based medicine.

The Bandolier team have also produced an excellent little book explaining medical evidence in more detail. (Bandolier 2006)

## Definitions: from Bandolier's EBM Glossary

**Systematic review**: *a summary of the medical literature that uses explicit methods to perform a thorough literature search and critical appraisal of individual studies and that uses appropriate statistical techniques to combine these valid studies.*

**Randomisation**: *method analogous to tossing a coin to assign patients to treatment groups.... Usually done by using a computer that generates a list of random numbers, which can then be used to generate a treatment allocation list.*

**Randomised controlled trial (RCT)**: *A group of patients is randomised into an experimental group and a control group. These groups are followed up for the variables/outcomes of interest.*

All the resources identified in this chapter are available at the web addresses given or via the National Library for Health (http://www.library.nhs.uk/). We will look more closely at the National Library for Health in Chapter 17.

## Reference

*Bandolier's little book of understanding medical evidence* (2006) Oxford: Oxford University Press.

# National Library for Health

---

**In this chapter**

- NLH: what it is
- NLH: what it contains

---

## 17.1 About the NLH

The National Library for Health at http://www.library.nhs.uk/ is not a type of information. It is an online resource where you can find many of the types of information we have been discussing throughout this book. You can use it as a 'one-stop shop' for electronic health information for all NHS staff.

The Library is an NHS funded 'library' of electronic resources and documents. Part of its vision is 'to deliver a modern equitable knowledge service to all NHS staff and those that deliver care to NHS patients'.

Much of the content is freely available to the general public, but some areas require an NHS Athens account. These resources are free to 'eligible users from within the "NHS Family" wherever they may be working. The term NHS Family is used to describe staff working for, or delivering services on behalf of, or in conjunction with, the NHS.'

You can self-register for NHS Athens from the NLH website. If you do this from a computer on the NHS network (e.g. from your workplace) it will be ready to use straight away. Registration from a non-NHS net computer takes some days to become effective.

# 17.2 Content provided by NLH

*Key content areas*

The main content areas are:

- **Evidence-based reviews**
  Resources providing the best available evidence for health care – including the Cochrane Library. You can search an individual resource or two or more simultaneously.
- **Guidance**
  Including **clinical guidelines**, which are 'designed to assist practitioner and patient on decisions about appropriate health care for specific clinical circumstances' and **care pathways**, which 'embed guidelines into everyday use for an individual patient.'
  Resources covered in this area include:
  - *National Library of Guidelines*
  - *Protocols and Care Pathways Library* (over 250 care pathways submitted by NHS organisations)
  - *Clinical Knowledge Summaries* – to help NHS professionals to manage common conditions seen in primary and first-contact care
  - *International Guidelines*
- **Specialist Libraries**
  The Specialist Libraries contain collections of electronic documents relevant to 'particular communities of practice', either a **particular health problem**, e.g.
  - Cancer
  - Diabetes
  - Gastroenterology and liver diseases
  - Learning disability
  - Mental health
  or a **type of health service**, e.g.
  - Complementary and alternative medicine
  - Emergency care
  - Palliative and supportive care
  - Surgery, theatres and anaesthesia
  or a **specific patient group**, e.g.
  - Child health
  - Ethnicity and health
  You can either go straight to a particular Specialist Library and browse the range of documents or search for something specific, or you can select two or more Libraries to search simultaneously.

If you are working in a specialist area and need quality assessed information, evaluated by a knowledgeable information professional, than the Specialist Libraries are for you.

■ **Books, journals and healthcare databases**

This section includes the following:

– *Healthcare databases*:

Seven healthcare databases (AMED, BNI, Embase, HMIC, PsychINFO, Medline from PubMed and CINAHL) which can be searched individually or in combination, when you are logged in with an NHS Athens ID.

– *My journals*

This is a gateway to a range of full text journals available to NHS staff. Because of the comprehensive nature of NLH many of the journals included here are medical rather than nursing so may not give you what you need. You can do a simple search in 'My Journals', but it is not a substitute for a database search as it only searches the past two years.

Details of print journals available from local NHS libraries are also available.

### *Other content*

Further useful content offered by NLH includes:

■ **Images**: six specialist databases of images, including the Virtual Pediatric Library.
■ **For patients**: including the NHS Direct Online Health Encyclopaedia of information on conditions, tests, treatments, operations and services, which can be printed out in leaflet form.
■ **Drugs**: including British National Formulary, British National Formulary for Children, and the National Electronic Library for Medicines.
■ **Health news**: including topics from NHS Choices and from BBC Health and a featured Document of the Week.

National Library for Health contains extensive resources covering all aspects of NHS work. This is its great strength, but can also make it difficult to navigate and to find material that is at the right level for undergraduate students to use. You will find that NHS Librarians use NLH as their first port of call in answering queries. It's also important to know that NLH is available to you throughout your working life, whether or not you are enrolled as a student and have access to the resources of a university. Spend some time finding your way around the site and exploring what NLH has to offer.

# CHAPTER 18

# What next?

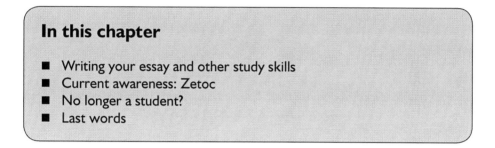

**In this chapter**

- Writing your essay and other study skills
- Current awareness: Zetoc
- No longer a student?
- Last words

We hope that the advice and guidance in this little book will have helped you to find information you need for any kind of academic assignment, to judge its quality and use it with confidence. We hope too that you look at our recommended websites and find at least some of them as useful as we do.

Better still, we hope that over time you will become confident of your own information skills and go on to find resources, print and electronic, for yourself. The world of information and media is constantly changing and developing. We have tried to ensure that the information we have given is up to date and accurate, but by the time you are reading this there will be many new websites and possibly new ways of accessing information. We hope that having mastered the principles of finding and using information you will be able to search out new resources for yourself.

## 18.1 Essay writing and related skills

Our focus has been on gathering information for an academic assignment and knowing how to evaluate and reference it properly. Unfortunately, this is the limit of our expertise! Your challenge now is to formulate your own ideas based on the information you have read, and to incorporate those ideas into your academic assignments.

Help on writing academic assignments is available to you from a number of sources.

Your university library will almost certainly have leaflets – printed or online – on topics such as essay writing, report writing, preparing presentations, and writing a dissertation. Have a look on its website or ask library staff.

Most academic libraries carry a range of 'study skills' books. There are many of these, mostly very general but also some written especially for health students. Here are a few that we particularly like.

A series of short books from the Open University:

Levin, P. and Topping, G. (2006) *Perfect presentations!* Maidenhead: Open University Press.

Levin, P. (2004). *Write great essays!* Maidenhead: Open University Press.

Levin, P. (2005) *Excellent dissertations!* Maidenhead: Open University Press.

*These three titles are from a series called 'Student-friendly guides' and they really are – simple advice clearly presented.*

Creme, P. and Lea, M. R. (2008) *Writing at university: a guide for students*, 3rd ed. Maidenhead: Open University Press.

*This book looks at the nature of academic writing and at different styles of writing for different purposes, and also has useful chapters on referencing and evaluating web resources.*

McMillan, K. and Weyers, J. (2007) *How to write essays and assignments.* Harlow: Pearson Education.

*This book includes note taking, essay planning, grammar and punctuation as well as writing techniques.*

McMillan, K. and Weyers, J. (2007) *How to write dissertations and project reports.* Harlow: Pearson Education.

*Includes planning research, applying research techniques, working with data and numbers, editing and revising.*

Northedge, A. (2005) *The good study guide.* Milton Keynes: Open University.

*This one covers learning styles, using computers, seminars, workshops and presentations, and handling numbers, as well as assignment writing.*

Cottrell, S. (2008) *The study skills handbook*, 3rd ed. Basingstoke: Palgrave Macmillan.

*Something of a classic, Stella Cottrell's book covers aspects such as time management, memory training and critical analytical thinking.*

A couple that are specially relevant for health studies:

Maslin-Prothero, S. (2005) *Baillière's study skills for nurses and midwives*, 3rd ed. Edinburgh: Baillière Tindall.

*This book covers many of the areas of concern to health students: reading and lectures, learning through reflection, portfolios, assignments and placements.*

Aveyard, H. (2007) *Doing a literature review in health and social care: a Practical Guide.* Maidenhead: Open University Press.
*This is a very comprehensive guide which would be particularly useful if you were doing a dissertation based on a literature review.*

## 18.2 Current awareness

If you don't want to be constantly searching databases, but you do want to be aware of new developments and newly published materials in your subject area, then a current awareness service is what you need. Current awareness is just another way of saying 'what's going on'. You may remember that in Chapter 11 we looked at a database called Zetoc. Zetoc has an amazing additional feature called 'Zetoc Alert'. The Alert enables you to choose some journal titles (from a list of over 20,000), create a list, and have the table of contents from all the journals on your list emailed to you as soon as they become available. You can have as many lists as you like, with up to 50 journals on each, but

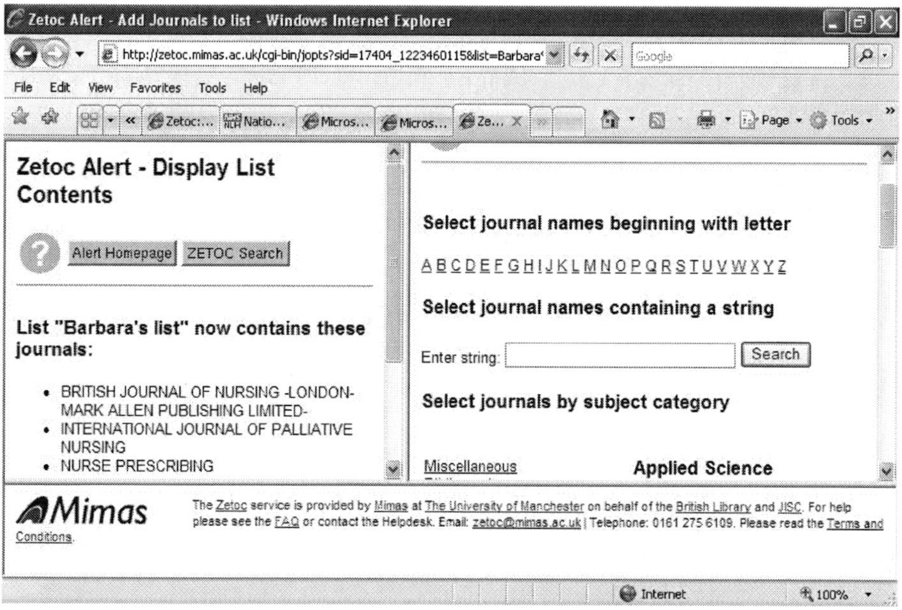

**Figure 18.1** Zetoc Alert. On the left, a simple list. On the right, the search screen with various options.

realistically you are more likely to follow up articles from just a few journals, so it's best to keep your list short.

To create a Zetoc Alert, from the database chose Alert, rather than Search. If this is your first list, you will be asked for an email address and have the opportunity to name your list. You will also be asked to choose whether or not you want to create links to the full record in the Zetoc database – a useful feature. You can then start to add either 'Journals' or 'Searches' to your list.

To add journals, you choose titles in one of three ways: from an A–Z list; by entering a string of words, which could be the journal title or just some words from it; or from pre-selected subject categories. Among subject categories, Medical Sciences and Medical Sciences (Diseases) form one of the largest. Each title you select is added to your list.

Another option is to add Author or Title Searches to your list. Zetoc Alert will then send you details of any article by that author or with those words in the title, whether or not it is from one of your chosen journals.

Your list will last for a year, at which point you can renew it, and you can add or remove journals at any point.

It takes only a few minutes to set up a list and then you can just sit back and wait for information to be delivered into your mail box.

## 18.3 No longer a student?

When you have handed in your last assignment, completed your course and gained your qualification, you will probably heave a huge sigh of relief and vow 'Never again!' But the reality is that nursing, midwifery and allied health are professions where it is essential to keep up to date. As a qualified practitioner you may find yourself working in a clinical area that is new to you and realise that you have a lot to learn. You will probably be back to studying again before you know it!

If you are working towards a specialist practitioner qualification and juggling the demands of work, home life and study, you will probably have periods of study interspersed with time away from study.

Now that you have learned some information skills, it's important not to lose them. Some ways of keeping up to date are given below.

### Don't lose touch with the library

Easier said than done – when no longer a student you won't have full access to the university library. Some libraries have schemes where former students can have limited membership for a small cost, or may offer reference-only facilities to NHS staff. It's always worth asking.

Investigate workplace libraries – even if you don't work for a large acute Trust you may well have access to its library.

If no 'physical' library is readily available to you, remember the 'virtual' library. The National Library for Health is intended to be a resource available to you throughout your working life.

### NLH for current awareness

In addition to the many useful features of the National Library for Health that we have referred to throughout the book, there is an area of NLH called 'My Library' which is well worth exploring. Here you can personalise information in various ways to make it easier for you to use. Zetoc Alert, as described above, is available via 'My Library', in the 'My Athens Resources' section. There is also a similar service called 'My Alerts' for journals in the NLH collection.

## 18.4 Last words

We hope you have enjoyed this little book, whether you read it through from beginning to end or just dipped in. Maybe you will remember later something we mentioned and dip in again! We want the information in this book to be useful to you, but above all we want you to have the confidence to find information for yourself. Finding information doesn't have to be lengthy and frustrating – it can be very satisfying, as we hope you'll see. There is always something new to find and your skills will constantly develop. You will surprise yourself!

If you carry away just one message from this book, let it be this: *Libraries and librarians are here to help you, so don't be afraid to ask!*

# How libraries are arranged

## Most multi-subject libraries use the Dewey system

In the Dewey system, all areas of knowledge are divided into 'classes', each of which is given a number. Within that class, more specific subjects are given more specific numbers, divided by a decimal point. The main classes and the numbers given to them are:

000 – Computer science, information, general works
100 – Philosophy and psychology
200 – Religion
300 – Social sciences
400 – Language
500 – Science
600 – Technology
700 – Arts and recreation
800 – Literature
900 – History and geography

Health-related subjects all come into the Technology or 600 class, so for example many nursing books will be in the 610 area, midwifery at 618, anatomy at 612 and so on. You could browse the shelves at these numbers and you are likely to see a range of books that would be useful to you. This might be a useful starting point, but if you depend only on this area you will be missing lots of other really useful stuff. For instance, books on health psychology will be in the 100 section; those on the sociology of health will be at 300.

To find all the areas that will be useful to you, you need to use the library catalogue.

# Most specialist health libraries use National Library of Medicine classification – or NLM

In NLM classification, the main classes have letters to identify them and then the more specific sections have numbers. NLM is really a couple of classes taken out of a general scheme and expanded to make them more useful for specialist health libraries – which is why you will find that many 'shelf-marks' start with the letters Q or W.

The main classes of NLM and the letters given to them are:

- **'Q' classes, known as the 'Preclinical Sciences'**:
  QS    Human Anatomy
  QT    Physiology
  QU    Biochemistry
  QV    Pharmacology
  QW    Microbiology and immunology
  QX    Parasitology
  QY    Clinical pathology
  QZ    Pathology
- **'W' classes for Medicine and related subjects**:
  W      Health professions
  WA    Public health
  WB    Practice of medicine
  WC    Communicable diseases
  WD    Disorders of systemic, metabolic or environmental origin, etc.
  WE    Musculoskeletal system
  WF    Respiratory system
  WG    Cardiovascular system
  WH    Blood and lymphatic systems
  WI     Digestive system
  WJ     Urogenital system
  WK    Endocrine system
  WL    Nervous system
  WM    Psychiatry
  WN    Radiology, diagnostic imaging
  WO    Surgery
  WP    Gynecology
  WQ    Obsterics
  WR    Dermatology
  WS    Paediatrics
  WT    Geriatrics, chronic disease
  WU    Dentistry, oral surgery

WV    Otolaryngology (ear, nose and throat)
WW   Ophthalmology
WX    Hospitals and other health facilities
WY    Nursing
WZ    History of medicine

As nursing has a main class of its own – WY – many of the books you need will be found there. But in the way in which most libraries use this scheme, nursing books may not all be together. Books on nursing a patient with a particular condition are shelved alongside other books on that condition – for example, a book on nursing care of a patient with a heart disease will be with other books on heart diseases at WG; books on nursing care of children with other books on paediatrics in the WS section.

To find all the areas that will be useful to you, you need to use the library catalogue.

# Index